Dr Peter Plichta was born in 1939 and studied chemistry, physics and biology. The author of many publications, he also has a number of patents to his credit. It was he who succeeded in synthesizing an oil from silicon – the fuel of the future for air and space travel. Dr Plichta had been carrying out intensive research in mathematics and natural philosophy for 15 years before he managed the decisive breakthrough in 1993.

GOD'S SECRET FORMULA

Deciphering the Riddle of the
Universe and the Prime Number Code

Peter
Plichta

ELEMENT
Shaftesbury, Dorset • Rockport, Massachusetts
Brisbane, Queensland

© Element Books Limited 1997
Text © 1995, by Albert Langen Georg Müller Verlag in der
F. A. Herbig Verlagsbuchhandlung GmbH, München

In collaboration with Walburga Posch

Published in Great Britain in 1997 by
Element Books Limited
Shaftesbury, Dorset SP7 8BP

Published in the USA in 1997 by
Element Books, Inc.
PO Box 830, Rockport, MA 01966

Published in Australia in 1997 by
Element Books Limited
for Jacaranda Wiley Limited
33 Park Road, Milton, Brisbane 4064

Cover design by Mark Slader
Page design by Roger Lightfoot
Typeset by Bournemouth Colour Press, Parkstone, Poole, Dorset
Printed and bound in U.S.A. by Edwards Brothers. Inc. Michigan

British Library Cataloguing in Publication
data available

Library of Congress Cataloging in Publication
data available

ISBN 1–86204–014–1

CONTENTS

1	The End of All Dogma	1
2	Chemistry and Passion	13
3	The Beginnings of a Research Scientist	25
4	Number and Plan	37
5	Space and the Riddle	49
6	Vision and Determination	61
7	The Final Question	75
8	Upside-down and Backwards	88
9	The Queen of the Sciences	102
10	Concerning Electrons and Prime Number Twins	113
11	Putting Bounds on the Infinite	125
12	The House of Cards That is Physics	137
13	The Law of Empty Space	149
14	Revelation	159
15	The Order Within Disorder	172
16	The Search for Reciprocal Geometry	186
17	God is Back!	199
	Epilogue	212
	Index	214

I would like to make a prediction: Before the end of this century, the century of scientific-critical alexandrinism, of the great harvests, of the final versions, a new development in the direction of inner values and spiritualism will overcome science's need for victories. The exact sciences are being pushed towards their doom by the increasing refinement of their inquiry and methods. (...)

But before this, the Faustian, eminently historical spirit will be confronted with a hitherto unknown, hitherto inconceivable task. A *Morphology of the Exact Sciences* will be written, which will investigate the inner correlation between all laws, terms and theories as forms and their significance in the development of Faustian culture. Theoretical physics, chemistry, mathematics as embodiment of a system of symbols – this will be the final ascendancy of the intuitive, ultimately religious approach over the mechanical understanding of the world.

The Decline of the West:
Outlines in a morphology of world history
Oswald Spengler

CHAPTER ONE

THE END OF ALL DOGMA

On the morning of 18 April 1994, a taxi driving through Frankfurt, Germany suddenly turned off Offenbacher Landstrasse and through the entrance to St Georgen College. The door opened and an excited Siberian husky leapt from the car, followed by two men who strode through the gate of the German Jesuit University at nine o'clock sharp. At Reception they requested that Professor Rupert Lay be informed that Dr Matheis and Dr Plichta had arrived for their appointment. Germany's most famous Jesuit appeared in a suit and tie a short time later. After he had briefly admired the husky, all three men proceeded to another of the university buildings, where they entered an office and took their seats.

It had been many years since I turned my back on the Catholic Church. In the course of my work on the essence and structure of infinity, however, religious aspects had increasingly impinged on my attention, particularly in recent years. I therefore got in touch with Professor Lay, a man of unique academic achievement. In addition to doctorates in philosophy and theology, he has a doctor's degree in physics, as well as a sound university education in psychology and business economics. He is known in professional circles as the author of a number of books, as a business and political consultant, and as a skilled psychoanalyst and rhetorician – a master of many trades who, incidentally, has earned a lot of money for his order. The important thing for me, however, was that he had a thorough knowledge of mathematics and chemistry.

Chemistry is the science of matter. Most matter exists in the form of chemical compounds made up of two or more of approximately 80 different stable elements. For reasons that will later be made clear, chemists have, with very few exceptions, never been at all interested in just why this should be the case.

Physics is the science of movement. Physicists are not interested in chemistry and chemists are not interested in physics. The question of the ultimate origin of all substance was formerly the sole domain of theology, of a Church that taught that a personal God created all matter out of nothing. Any concept of a material 'proto-substance' would eventually have provoked the question: 'But where did that substance come from?' Such questions therefore never arose – just as it later became normal in science to avoid uncomfortable questions by feigning ignorance or indifference.

After the Church had long since lost its power, the question of the origin of matter was taken up in the 20th century curiously enough by physicists and not by chemists – creation out of 'nothing' was replaced by the extremely dubious theory of the Big Bang. This initially aroused only laughter; laughter increasingly gave way to acceptance, and finally jubilation and admiration. Theory was soon transformed into undisputed 'fact', and this version of events is now even taught in primary schools. I was aware that Professor Lay considers both theories – creation out of nothing and creation out of a Big Bang – to be hopelessly wrong, as I do. If the origin of the world remains a mystery, then a solution must be waiting somewhere to be discovered, regardless of how deep it is buried. That is demanded by logic.

I sat in front of Professor Lay, a man familiar with this problem, and who was aware that I had thrown some light into the recesses of this secret. It is generally assumed in our age that scientific discoveries are made in those places where it is possible for the taxpayer to see huge amounts of money being swallowed – in universities and state-supported research programmes. However, this is a fallacy. The frontiers of human knowledge have always been pushed back by the individual, not by teams or by heavily-subsidized research programmes. This individual has also usually not been a specialist in his or her

2

field, and is much more likely to be a person dedicated to research, who can pursue the quest for truth without the pressures and constraints of institutionalized science, and who can furthermore combine expert knowledge from a variety of disciplines.

Such a scholar was Gottfried Leibniz, who studied philosophy and law and later became an alchemist and physicist. His unravelling of calculations to infinity made him one of the greatest mathematicians in history. At the same time, he was also a diplomat, theologian, historian, technological inventor and author in a wide range of subjects.

I first noticed a desire to get right to the heart of a problem when, at the age of 11, I got hold of a book on chemistry. This desire later brought me into contact with almost all branches of science so that I felt I was finally in a position to rival the versatility of Dr Faustus himself.

Now, 40 years later, I was sitting beside a man with the professional competence and human capacity to accurately assess the content and implications of my work. On the desk in front of him were my two books, which I had given him some weeks previously and which he had since read. I have had to confront quite a few examiners in my time. First it was a hoard of university professors during my many exams. Later I was obliged on countless occasions to accept personal assessments of my theoretical work. Ideally they should all have served as support and encouragement for my research, but very often they aroused in me nothing but holy wrath. Such a reaction nonetheless also gave me the determination to succeed.

The time in which I was forced to rely on the opinions of others is now gone. I know I have found the indisputable solution to the puzzle at the centre of this material universe: the archetypal struggle between theology and science has been resolved.

Dr Matheis opened the conversation. 'Professor Lay, at our last meeting on February 16th you were kind enough to agree to read Mr Plichta's two books and be prepared to comment on them.'

I suddenly had a very strange sensation. I was completely at peace with myself. I had a curious feeling that an invisible person was standing behind me. I felt the ice-cold radiance of truth.

Professor Lay answered, reading from his notes, 'My comments on Mr Plichta's books are that 1) the books are fascinating to read; 2) the contents are faultless from a mathematical point of view; and 3) Mr Plichta's scientific research constitutes the first fundamental statement ever made on our concept of the physical world: everything before Plichta – from Newton to Einstein – has only been theory.'

There was a deadly silence in the room. The cold behind me had disappeared.

I had been hoping for a positive response from Professor Lay, but I had not expected such an uncompromising and forthright verdict on the tradition of physics.

A concept of the physical world can only be accurate to the degree permitted by the contemporary state of mathematics – a fact well known to all major thinkers of previous centuries. Today almost nobody is aware of it.

Most readers will remember their maths lessons at school with horror. In fact, all that actually remains with most of us after thirteen years' schooling is usually little more than basic arithmetic. As a result, interest in mathematics among the general public is close to zero. Those who require a more detailed study of maths – perhaps on the way to a degree in physics or chemistry – do not seem in my opinion to feel the slightest degree of wonder at the fact that 'the book of nature is written in mathematics' – as Galileo Galilei put it.

Even those who study mathematics tend not to comprehend it as a finite subject in itself. Maths students are in fact told nothing of the fact that mathematics has been considered 'complete' since the end of the 19th century. This view is not affected by the discoveries made in individual areas of mathematics during the 20th century. Although the majority of modern mathematical publications do actually manage to make a rather dignified impression, behind this facade there is usually little more than pretentious formalism and meaningless verbiage. They serve to further the career of the author and no more.

The conventional phrase 'the concept of the physical world' also poses major problems for the student of mathematics because the mathematics he uses is taught by the professors as an invention that would not exist at all had it not been created by the human mind.

Mathematics is the science of numbers, shapes and the relations between them. Its task is to postulate universally true propositions and to furnish proofs. It is therefore very closely connected with logic, the science of truth. To introduce dogma – special or even generally applicable axioms of belief – into mathematics would involve a break with the tradition of logic. And this is precisely what has happened.

The mathematician J W Dedekind, in his far-reaching treatise of 1887 *What are Numbers and What Do They Mean?*, described numbers as a conceptual creation of the human mind. This attitude found general acceptance, although there is no proof to support it. It has indeed attained such a stature that any mathematician convinced of the real existence of numbers might be declared insane by his fellows. However, for the really great mathematicians of the past – including Newton, Leibniz, Euler, Gauss and Hermite – it was natural to link numbers and the numerical sequence towards infinity with divinity and eternal existence. According to current mathematical thinking, these true geniuses should be issued with a posthumous certificate of insanity. Today's experts, of course, do not go that far and only consider them 'dated' in this respect. But that is total nonsense, for truth is totally independent of time.

In 20th-century terms, mathematics is therefore held only to be a very sophisticated mental activity which – by a wonderful coincidence – can also describe the real world with the numbers it 'invents'. But no more than that.

In the course of my first conversation with Professor Lay I had told him that the world does not function according to a plan preordained by a divine act of creation out of nothing, nor by the coincidence and randomness of a Big Bang. It operates instead according to a plan inherent in the nature and structure of infinity. Professor Lay then asked, 'What do you mean by the term *infinity*?'

I explained. 'By infinity I mean the sum of all that can be conceived as infinite and that does not infringe logic. This includes space, time and – as I can prove – the set of all successive numbers 0, 1, 2, 3, ..., which never ends. Infinity

5

thus has a three-fold nature. The parallel to the concept of God that prevails in the West – in the Persons of Father, Son and Holy Ghost – is not only remarkable but also fascinating from a mathematical point of view because the third infinite dimension, numbers, does in fact contain some very profound information: the pattern of distribution of the prime numbers. As numbers increase in size, the prime numbers decrease in frequency.'

I continued, warming to the theme, 'Even as a 15-year-old, Gauss suspected that the decrease in frequency of the prime numbers obeys a simple mathematical law, namely the natural logarithm to base $e = 2.718 \ldots$ – Euler's number. It turned out to be extremely difficult to prove this supposition, but about one hundred years later, in 1896, the French mathematician Jacques Hadamard astonished the experts with a solution to the Prime Number Law. The scientific world of the time missed a unique opportunity to link the prime numbers to physics.'

Professor Lay interrupted me: 'Could you explain that a bit more, please?'

'Well,' I said, 'all physical processes – radioactive dis-integration, the barometric altitude ratio, escape velocity or entropy, for example – obey laws based on the natural logarithm. Since the decrease in frequency of the prime numbers is also linked to the natural logarithm, our physical world must be the result of the distribution of prime numbers.'

I could see the tension mounting in Professor Lay, and with his next question he showed that he had fully understood me.

'How is it that I know nothing of this, although I am a physicist?'

'The answer is very simple,' I told him. 'Physics students learn to work with the natural logarithm without once being encouraged to look at why the fundamental mathematical operation – the integral of 1 divided by x – produces the natural logarithm. Physicists have simply accepted this result of mathematical research without asking themselves how physical processes can possibly be described by a logarithm based on the mathematical constant e. In the field of mathematics the situation is every bit as bad: nobody is interested in asking how the decrease in prime numbers (or even how the prime

6

numbers themselves) can have anything to do with Euler's number.

The memory of this first conversation had passed through my mind in an instant. For some moments there was complete silence.

Dr Matheis took up the theme once more: 'How should we proceed from here?'

'We must discuss how to overcome the enormous resistance encountered by anything really new,' I suggested. 'In science, new discoveries have always taken a very long time – often one or two generations – to assert themselves. So it would do no good at all to proceed in the normal way by communicating the new findings to the scientific world through publications and lectures. Moreover, the editorial offices of the most prestigious publications are staffed by scholars who only accept work from elite universities. It would be quite pointless to approach the elite universities with this knowledge, though, since the central question of the mystery of existence is never asked in such institutions. It would be met by total incomprehension. The ceaseless celebration of past glories has made everyone blind to the most fundamental questions.'

We went on to discuss how scientific discoveries are only worth while when they can be used for the benefit of humankind. For a long time the general public has had a very critical attitude towards rapid progress in technology. Scientists have increased and multiplied like mice in an overflowing granary, financed by subsidies provided by the taxpayers whether they like it or not. This also means that science itself has been reduced to a mere livelihood. Such a venal attitude, which is always accompanied by indifference to more universal questions, has given rise to a system that has elevated an extremely dubious concept of the world to the status of dogma. Theoretical physicists, nuclear physicists or astrophysicists who dare to express doubt about this theory are barred from professional advancement in the university hierarchy. The fact that all genuine scientific progress can only have its origins in doubt and criticism has either been completely forgotten or consciously suppressed. Yet such creative criticism is only worth while when aimed at the prevailing doctrines of the present.

History also shows, however, that progress in the end is not hindered by ignorance; it can at most be greatly delayed.

'There can be no question of tolerating years of delay,' I declared. 'The deciphering of the prime number puzzle is a decisive intellectual breakthrough in the problems confronting all of humankind. Humanity needs help now!'

We live in a period of major intellectual upheaval. Ten years ago nobody could have imagined the demolition of the walls of barbed wire that then ran through the heart of Europe. The full extent of lies and distortions under the totalitarian Communist regimes was overwhelming. However, because no sound intellectual preparation had been made, the collapse of the system only brought the freedom to adopt the capitalist system. Perhaps now the question arises as to whether capitalism is not also doomed to extinction. It was quite clear to the three of us that the materialistic and rapacious capitalism prevailing in the West also poses real dangers to humanity.

Communism propagated by Russia is atheistic. Capitalism with its essentially materialist character is also atheistic, as is our picture of the physical universe at the end of the second millennium.

Prophets of various hues have for years been predicting an approaching transformation of our picture of the cosmos. But they have not told us where the spiritual foundation for this transformation should come from.

Mathematics and logic are the basis of all thought. If the basis of thought is rife with errors, tragic consequences for our ideas of the cosmos and for our philosophical and theological precepts are inevitable. The discovery of a blueprint of existence will necessarily sound the death-knell for atheism. If the world did not evolve from a primal explosion and the human mind is therefore not a product of chance, absolutely everything must be thought out afresh.

By the time we finished our discussion we had all sensed the importance of making this new knowledge accessible to a broad public, and thus to the 'man on the street'. This is the only real way to ensure that my discoveries spread and bear fruit while there is still time to solve the problems confronting humankind.

But as we rose to leave we had still not come to any conclusion over how this state of affairs could be brought about.

Will it ever be possible to communicate what I know to the general public? Isn't the 'man on the street' primarily involved in managing his day-to-day existence? Could he find room in his leisure time for chemical and mathematical problems?

As I took my leave I shook Professor Lay's hand. Fascinating as our conversation was, I still remained sceptical. My theoretical research had cost me enormous reserves of strength. The creative struggle of wresting the secret from the world is finally finished. I am immeasurably happy to have accomplished the task. But at the same time I feel that my difficult mission is surely not yet over. I suddenly notice a quick flicker in Professor Lay's eyes. A hint of a smile and a short nod of the head signals: 'You can manage it!' Coming from this extremely aloof intellectual and forceful, if also reserved, representative of the Roman Catholic Church, the reaction seemed to me the ultimate in emotional commitment.

I suddenly felt new courage returning. I had gone to visit a theologian because the blueprint for the universe I had discovered inevitably involves the question of the existence of God. A fascinating thought sprang into my mind. It is not so important whether the 'man in the street' is interested in chemistry or mathematics. The normal person can switch on a light, start a car or turn on a television without worrying his head about the fundamentals of alternating currents, internal combustion or the function of a cathode tube. Perhaps he also does not need to read maths books in order to comprehend and accept the significance of my discoveries.

Standard mathematics and natural sciences are extremely complicated. Even as a child I was fascinated by Goethe's view that all great notions have to be simple. The majestic equations in textbooks have always seemed to me to be a smoke-screen for human helplessness, and this suspicion has now been vindicated. The solution to the quest for the origins of the material world is characterised by simplicity, clarity and an irresistible elegance. It must be revealed to people in a book. The results of complex scientific analysis and discussion now mean that an answer can be given to the simplest and deepest questions of humanity.

Which are the questions that all people ask at some time in their lives? The questions are: 'Who am I?', 'Where do I come from?', 'Why does the world exist?' and the most decisive question of all, 'Is there a God?' The world of science has so far been unable to provide answers to these questions. Perhaps this is why, in their suppressed rage, scientists unconsciously make everything so complicated. They dismiss this uncomfortable question with the excuse that 'It is not our responsibility.'

Theologians are convinced that the existence of God can be proved only through sacred scripture. Religious leaders have repeatedly attempted to find other verifications of God. The attempts did not get very far, and necessity then became a virtue – faith was given a higher status than knowledge.

The answers to the above questions therefore remain obscure. The only certain truths of this world have been passed down to us by great teachers such as Buddha, Lao-tse and Jesus.

The revelation of a universal plan will force scientists and theologians to review their dogmatic vanity and give every lay person the chance to enquire into the matter to whatever degree they like. Each individual will thus be able to declare his or her independence of self-appointed authority. This will logically lead to individual responsibility and freedom. As long as the true facts of a matter remain unknown, the door remains open to all kinds of idle talk. When the truth is revealed, clarity and peace should prevail.

Most of my work in the first half of 1994 was devoted to examining the most important mathematical theorems in order to discover whether they were just different physical extensions of one and the same thing – the prime numbers. By June I had discovered the answer to the question. I knew then that the creaking edifice of that most vain of all sciences – mathematics – would soon collapse.

More lies have been told in chemistry than in any other science. Nowhere is it possible to encounter so much bombastic bravado as in physics. And nowhere is there near as much foolishness as in biology, with its subdivision of medicine, since in no other area has so much total nonsense been propounded – and again forgotten – as in the science of living matter. In all three natural sciences, the current errors – and by this I mean not only minor but also major, and especially the most preposterous, errors – soon disappear from the textbooks and are replaced by new ones. We therefore always live with the errors that happen to be valid at the present moment.

In mathematics, on the other hand, it is alleged that no errors have ever been made because in this science only formal proof is accepted. Yet such an argument quite blatantly suppresses the question of how some extremely profound speculations exist in the world of numbers that can either be proven beyond doubt or conversely elude a definite solution.

I spent two weeks coming to terms with the ramifications of the approaching collapse of mathematics. For that science will sink as surely as the world's proudest battleship would sink after being struck by a salvo of torpedoes.

A fundamental and hitherto undiscovered harmony permeates mathematics. I can now prove conclusively what Europe's great thinkers – from Pythagoras, Plato, Bruno, Leibniz and Gauss to Einstein and Sommerfeld – could only guess at: without the existence of numbers as objects in reality there could not be a universe. I reach for the telephone and dial the number of Professor Rupert Lay.

I tell him that the collapse of accepted mathematical dogma will usher in an entirely new scientific situation. He replies, 'I am aware of that, Mr Plichta.'

I ask him, 'Would you be prepared to speak about the inevitable collapse of the dogmas of mathematics in front of a television camera?'

'Of course,' comes his answer.

I am once more aware of a cold sensation at my back. I hear my own stunned words form the question: 'But you know that when one single central dogma falls, from that day on all statements of "truth" by human beings will appear in a very dubious light.'

'That is correct,' replies the clergyman.

'But you are a Catholic priest and the Catholic Church is entirely ensnared in "accepted truths," or dogma', I insist.

'But why does the Catholic Church have to have dogma? The other Christian Churches manage quite well without it,' I hear him reply – to my amazement.

I know that my next question, and his reply, will constitute a step into a new age.

'Are you also prepared to stand in front of a camera and state that on the collapse of all accepted mathematical theory, which corresponds to a symbol of the extent of human delusion, the Catholic Church will have no other option but to distance itself rigorously from its own dogma and to consign it to a bygone period of history?'

'Of course,' he replied for a second time.

CHAPTER TWO

CHEMISTRY AND PASSION

At my birth, an event occurred which had such a powerful effect on my mother that she continued to recall it for the next 20 years.

When she awoke from the anaesthetic on 21 October 1939 the chief surgeon, ward physicians and nurses from the Fabricius Clinic came to her bed and laid a baby boy in each of her arms. At that very moment the heavens opened and – according to my mother – a brilliantly warm beam of light forced its way through the heavy rainclouds and shone brightly on the heads of the newborn infants. One of the sisters present exclaimed: 'A miracle!' Another knelt and crossed herself. 'Something very special is in store for these two boys,' a doctor declared. My mother in her superstitious way and the pious sisters were only too willing to believe this prediction, and the nuns then suggested that I be given the name Peter. And, because the name Paul has been a traditional name in our family for generations, we twins were later baptized with the names of the apostles Peter and Paul.

Prophecies on the occasion of the birth of children have been described many times in history. Six months before the birth of Jean François Champollion, the man who deciphered ancient Egyptian hieroglyphs, the 'magician' Jacqou had predicted that the completely bedridden expectant mother would soon recover. He also prophesied the birth of a boy who 'would one day attain such renown as would endure for centuries' (C W

Ceram). When Champollion was 11 years old, the famous mathematician and physicist Fourier invited him to his house and showed the boy his Egyptian collection. The boy was fascinated to see his first papyrus fragments and asked Fourier, 'Can you read that?' When the old man replied that he could not, the young Champollion declared 'Well, I shall read it when I am grown up!'

The year 1939 was one of the most fateful in human history. In February the great nuclear scientist Otto Hahn published an article containing the proof that uranium atoms could be split. Two hundred years previously the father of modern chemistry, Antoine de Lavoisier, had described the elements as entities that could *not* be divided further. Ever since then the indivisibility of the atoms that constitute all elements had been proved again and again in experiments and finally turned into dogma.

Otto Hahn had thus shown a 'known fact' of natural science to be false. The discovery in 1939 led to the explosion of the first three atomic bombs six years afterwards. Some years later a mathematician managed to work out the concept of how atomic bombs could be utilised to ignite heavy hydrogen and lithium. Hydrogen bombs, the power of which exceeds almost anything we can imagine, are still even now primed for explosion. The triggering programmes are ciphered in prime numbers. The whole of humankind is in danger.

Growing up with a twin brother proved to be extremely important for my development. The 'twin syndrome' has accompanied me through my life.

I had been greatly looking forward to my first day at school, and the excitement had kept me awake the night before the big event. When finally we set out on our way to school I began dragging my mother by the arm to pull her forward. On the other hand, my brother – who had been quietly weeping for some time – now let out a wail of fear, threw himself on the ground and attempted to drag my mother back by the other arm. Passers-by were puzzled to see how one boy kept throwing himself on the pavement, received a smacking and continued to be dragged on, while the other was eagerly attempting to tug the mother forward. On the way back, the situation was reversed. I was now crying and my brother was eagerly pulling my mother towards home. We had arrived at the school to be

14

told that lessons had been postponed for six months because of a coal shortage.

I was already able to read by the time I went to school, whereas my brother refused to learn to read or write one single word. He showed no interest in his studies through the whole time at school, and all the punishment administered by our parents seemed to have no effect on his behaviour.

Our parents slowly began to recognise how fundamentally different our characters were. I read as much as I could while my brother never picked up a book. I became the teacher's pet, my brother sat in the classroom and never opened his mouth. Despite these clear differences we were always dressed the same and everywhere we went and were asked for our names we would stand up straight beside each other, stick out our chests and reply: 'Our names are Peter and Paul!'

The usual response to this was: 'Peter and Paul – one works well, one not at all.'

The years following the war were extremely difficult. My father was an engineer and was also keenly interested in many other branches of science. He was always experimenting around the house. At one stage he had collected so much rancid fat as even at this time of general hunger to be considered inedible. One day he boiled the fat together with diluted caustic soda in a giant cooking-pot on the kitchen stove in order to make soap. He had manufactured the soda himself from sodium hydroxide tablets. These tablets were stored in a strangely-shaped bottle with the wonderful label

NaOH Sodium Hydroxide pure state

The bottle was sealed with a cork that smelt of paraffin. I would often stand in the cellar and look at the white tablets, which my father had said could damage the cornea of the eye and cause blindness. But the word that plays a central role in this book – the concept that was to dominate my life – had not yet been spoken. A few years would pass before I heard for the first time the word *chemistry*!

Because things went so well for me at school, my relatives

15

soon began to forecast that Peter would one day become a professor, or perhaps even a great thinker. On the other hand, it was predicted that Paul would one day be very rich. Both predictions were to be fulfilled. Peter became a scientist and Paul married the heiress to a fortune which amounted to thousands of millions of dollars. My love was for chemistry while my brother's was for the wealth that derived from the chemical industry.

Our parents were completely helpless in view of the difference in our temperaments. Father never even asked about what we had learned at school, whereas mother was interested in homework and school grades to the point of obsession. That the asymmetry of the fraternal twins had a very natural cause never dawned on my parents. Their helplessness could clearly be seen in their explanation that Peter had taken from Paul all the nutrition available in the mother's womb and that it was only right that he compensated for this now by helping his brother with his homework. I always held this story about the womb to be absurd. I considered my brother entirely different to me, and I would have been utterly indifferent to him had I not had a certain peculiar but nonetheless strong sensation of being linked to this 'stranger' by an invisible yet indestructible bond.

I was not able to take the entrance exam to the Lessing Secondary School in Düsseldorf because I happened to be sick at the time. Paul therefore went to the examination alone but afterwards was not able to remember the questions that had been set. He unexpectedly passed the test, whereas in the repeat examination I had great difficulty with the arithmetic tasks. There were only very simple three-step arithmetic problems, but we had not yet done this kind of thing at school. In the usual circumstances I would have failed the test had not my arithmetic grades from the primary school certificate been so good.

An old white-haired gentleman took me into the corner of the school conference room. I later learned that he was not only a teacher of maths and physics but also an astronomer. He invited me to sit on his knee.

He said, 'Young man, tell me something about numbers.'

'The numbers begin with 1, 2, 3, or with 0, 1, 2, 3, and

16

continue through the decimal system by adding a 0 to make 10, 100, 1,000, 10,000 and so on.'

'But how do the numbers go on?' the old man asked.

I replied: 'Then there is a hundred thousand, then a million, then a thousand million, then a billion, then a thousand billion, then a trillion ...'

'And when do the numbers end?'

'Never,' I said.

'But why not? Surely they have to end sometime.'

'Numbers never end because they're infinite.'

'Do you know of anything else that is infinite?'

'Yes,' I replied. 'Space and time.'

He laid his hands on my head and said: 'Young man, you can go now.'

One day I discovered in my father's desk small packages of paper strips which were marked 'Merck Litmus Paper'. I asked my father what they were. He took me into the kitchen, filled one glass with water and added some vinegar. He fetched a lump of bicarbonate of soda from the scullery and dissolved it in another glass of water. He then took both red and blue litmus papers and dipped them alternately into the acid and base solutions. I observed the colour changes with wonder.

'What is that?' I wanted to know. 'What is it called?'

He smiled and answered: 'That's chemistry.'

I had never heard the word before, but a few days later the word turned up a second time. My parents had taken Paul and me around the Old Town of Düsseldorf and in the window of a shop selling optical instruments and toys, such as model railways and construction sets, I first read the word *chemistry*. A Kosmos chemistry set was on display in the window with a price tag of DM20. Fortunately, my eleventh birthday was approaching. I was scarcely able to wait for the day and was very much afraid that a quarrel might have disturbed the domestic scene by then – as too often happened in my parents' house – which would mean that the birthday present would be forfeited.

But everything happened just as I had longed for. My father drove me to Ziem the optician's during his lunch break and bought me the chemistry set. Afterwards he took me back to school. I arrived late and barged straight into the Latin class with a shout: 'Paul, I've got the chemistry set!'

That evening I immediately started experimenting. However, within only a few days I was already deeply disappointed. Something was missing from the instructions manual, something I could not have known about but could only guess: the chemical formulae were missing. That situation was finally remedied through my acquaintance with an older pupil to whom I was able to speak about my problems. He lent me the standard work of all young German chemists at the time – Römpp: *Practical Chemical Experiments*. In it were all the chemical formulae. Now I was finally satisfied.

Some time later I got hold of a proper chemistry textbook for the first time. I learned that all matter is made up of atoms and that there are different types of atoms. I immediately grasped how the entire universe was composed of certain types of matter which scientists call chemical elements. Numbered with the cardinal numbers 1, 2, 3, 4 ..., they are divided into groups (vertically) and periods (horizontally) according to similarity of characteristics. The chart showing all the chemical elements arranged in rows of sixteen is called the Periodic Table.

For weeks on end I scoured this book, finding out all about nitric acid, rare earths and radioactivity. I felt as if I had already known all these things but had only forgotten about them for some time – as if I were remembering something.

But one day the boy with whom I had been able to exchange notes on chemistry disappeared from the school and there was no longer anybody with whom I could discuss these things – apart from myself. Nobody would have been interested – neither my father nor my teachers – had I claimed as a ten-year-old that I was able to handle chemical formulae just as the young Mozart had been able to handle musical composition.

One year later I received a radio set and a radio valve with a potential difference of approximately 16 volts. As interesting as the experiments with the valve were, the small silicon crystal in the radio set fascinated me much more. When it came in contact with the tip of a wire, it was possible to receive distant radio stations through this crystal detector without any need for battery power. I applied myself to the question why the power of a silicon crystal could not be used to rectify high frequency alternating currents, instead of the cumbersome method with the radio valve.

I later learned that the American physicist J Bardeen had been awarded the Nobel Prize for exploiting this idea. He later changed his field of work and again received the Nobel Prize in 1972 for his research in the area of nuclear magnetic resonance spectroscopy. Using this method of spectroscopy, I was destined to be the first scientist to prove the existence of asymmetric twin atoms in silicon hydride and germanium hydride compounds in 1968. This was an essential prerequisite for my subsequent theoretical work. While carrying out these measurements I would recall my small silicon crystal – for transistors are manufactured from silicon or germanium.

The not-quite-11-year-old had discovered the word *chemistry*, and the following years would be characterized by my involvement in this science. In time I managed to assemble a complete laboratory.

My bent for theoretical problems has always been linked to the joy of experiment. Such a duality has accounted for many of the great successes in chemistry over the 19th and 20th centuries. Just as the Renaissance introduced a new era through the extraordinary talents of its craftsmen, artists, architects and engineers, experimental chemistry has radically changed our world over the past two hundred years. The young Peter vowed to use the skills of his hands in obeisance to this tradition. Later, the director of a chemistry institute would say that these hands reminded him of those of Emil Fischer, and that this winner of the Nobel Prize is capable of making crystals even from Swiss cheese.

With these same hands I very shortly learned to appreciate the power unleashed by a chemical explosion. One constantly reads stories of how young people mix chemicals and thereby cause serious accidents. I was fortunate as a young boy in that I made a really stupid mistake which made me realise that it is not the danger of the chemicals that is underestimated but rather the stupidity and manual clumsiness of would-be chemists.

Paul and I had received the present of our first balloon at a fair. I suspected that the gas inside was not the rather expensive helium, but hydrogen – element number 1 – which is much cheaper. The next day I decided to find out which gas was contained in the balloon. While my parents were having their afternoon nap, I untied the knot on the balloon, opened the door of the kitchen stove where a briquette fire was glowing, and carefully released a small quantity of gas from the balloon straight into the stove. When nothing happened, I released about half of the balloon's gas. There was a sudden and terrible bang. The heavy steel plate that covered the stove for an area of half a square metre was thrown into the air by the blast. I flew across the kitchen before finally landing under the table. I lay there black as a coalman having realized precisely why a hydrogen–air mixture is called detonating gas. The door between the kitchen and the bedroom opened slowly. My father popped his nose through a small opening and shouted back: 'Herta, he's still alive.'

In their joy that nothing had happened to me, my parents even forgot the thrashing that was standard for such occasions.

From then on I had a very special attitude to explosive materials. Without the experience gained in my youth with explosives and rocket fuel, I would never have been so confident in carrying out my work with silicon hydride later at the university. Chemists learn absolutely nothing about explosives during their studies, with the result that virtually none of them know much about the subject.

My first experiments with explosives were carried out using home-made electrical triggering devices, for I was aware that it would be much too dangerous to light fuses. The large garden and the factory yard behind our house made an ideal testing site in the evening and at weekends. I found it very amusing to sit at the kitchen table busily putting the finishing touches to a new bomb, wrapping everything up with insulating tape, while my mother stood at the stove cooking. I would then take my switchboard and a coil of cable, put a few tools in my trouser pocket and walk out the door. My mother would shout after me: 'Peter, dinner's almost ready.'

'It won't take long,' I would shout back. And it really did not take very long. All I had to do was link the bomb to the priming wire, roll out 25 metres of cable and connect the cable to the switchboard. I would activate a throw-over switch, test the

20

voltage, press the button on a bedside lamp and hear the fearful roar of the explosion. I would then roll up my cable, grab the switchboard and run back to the house. My mother would say, 'Some day the police will pay us a visit.'

I was given the money to buy the chemicals all those years by my mother, who accomplished the marvellous feat of providing for all the Plichtas, a housemaid and a dog from DM400 a month. I also helped myself by collecting waste paper and bits of scrap metal. My money would go to the Bären Pharmacy and to a chemicals dealer.

With a mixture of potassium chlorate and sugar, solid-fuel rockets could be made. When I ignited the propellant charge that had been jammed in a vice, the rockets would shoot up with a howl. I dreamt of sitting on a rocket and flying to the sky.

At the age of 13, I asked for another book by Römpp for Christmas: *Organic Chemistry in the Test Tube*. It cost DM8 and it was given to me as a present. I spent Christmas poring over this new book, in which the introduction begins with the following words:

> In the year of grace 1675 the French chemist and 'Docteur en Médecine' Lémery wrote an illuminating work entitled *Cours de Chymie* that has run to many editions and has been translated into most living and dead languages. In this book the world of matter was for the first time divided into three major categories ...

This sentence awakened my interest in the history of chemistry. Nothing is ever heard of the history of chemistry at our universities. On the contrary, chemists are collectively ashamed of their history which is peopled by magicians, charlatans and mystics. Over the centuries a few great chemists attempted to free the young science from the label of fraud. But in no other science – to quote the words used by Lutz Graf Schwerin von Krosigk when talking about alchemy – and at no other time (even before elections and after fishing expeditions) have so many lies been told as in chemistry.

A chemical experiment carried out by a boy with a chemistry set differs in no way from the same reaction carried out in the laboratory of a chemistry institute. When, for example, a colourless solution of a material A is mixed with another colourless solution of a material B and a thick, blue deposit

21

immediately forms, the postulation is made that this happens because A is reacting with B. Why precisely this is so, why this will also happen at the other end of the universe, and why it will continue to happen in the infinitely distant future – these are all questions that remain unanswered. Such questions are not even asked in the first place. They did not occur to me at that time either. There was so much written about all the things we know that for some time I did not notice how much we did not know.

My interest was also beginning to extend to the field of physics, and when I was about 15 I encountered a very unusual problem: the problem of electrons. An atom always consists of a nucleus and negatively charged particles, called electrons, which move around the nucleus as planets move around the sun. When two atoms are chemically linked, the chemist links them in his mind and in his diagrams by a stroke. The chemical bond is, in fact, effected by two electrons from the different atoms that hold each other. They are called electron pairs or twins. This pairing of electrons is one of the foundations of chemistry. Electron pair bonding is the reason why different atoms join to form molecules.

The physicist is not concerned with the creation of bonds between different atoms but rather with precise observation of the movement of electrons. Electrons can break away from the atom in certain situations – for instance, in a television tube.

Chemists and physicists therefore observe the behaviour of electrons from totally different perspectives. This is why completely different statements are made about what is clearly the same thing.

In electron physics, electrons are particles with the same electric charge which are mutually repellent and could never get it into their heads to come together and form a pair of electron twins.

When I had fully comprehended this contradiction I realised something very significant. Had I been only a chemist, I would have been totally indifferent to the physics of electrons because electron pairing is a proven fact. If, on the other hand, I had been only a physicist, I would have been equally indifferent to the chemistry of electrons because the repellent forces of two electrons is also a fact. My problem is that I was apparently going to become both – a chemist and a physicist.

Obviously my passion for the natural sciences was going to have consequences in the classroom. The biology teacher declared once – after rambling on for a confused 30 minutes about the mysterious substance chlorophyll – that no pupil in the class would be able to explain how the green vegetable dye could be isolated from leaves. Only a genius would be able to provide the correct answer. He then declared that geniuses had died out.

At that point I stood up and declared curtly: 'You crush green leaves with sand in a mortar, then boil the paste with alcohol. Then filter and draw off the alcohol. The chlorophyll is contained in the residue.'

The biology teacher exclaimed in a snarl that I must have read that somewhere, and that I was certainly no genius. I replied that he was much too stupid to judge that. The classroom was in uproar.

An almost similar scene occurred at the same time in the physics lesson. The teacher had gone on and on about Ohm's Law. The physicist Georg Simon Ohm discovered that the flow of electric current (ampere), resistance (ohm) and voltage (volt) are related to each other according to the following equation:

$$ohm = \frac{volt}{ampere} \quad or \quad resistance = \frac{voltage}{current}$$

The whole nature of electricity is wrapped up in this equation. The discovery caused a lot of trouble, however, for poor old Ohm. While Ohm was visiting Munich University, the professors 'proved' to the visitor that the laws of electricity are much too complicated to be expressed in an equation with only three letters. Then after he had returned from Munich the long arm of the disciplinary authority threatened him with dismissal.

Our physics teacher naturally uttered not a syllable in reference to this history. He asked instead whether anybody in the class could express the essence of Ohm's law in a single sentence. Whoever could do this must be a genius. When nobody else volunteered, I stood up.

'The special feature of this equation is that if only one of the three dimensions is set at 1, the remaining two must be either equal or reciprocal.'

Our physics teacher was impressed and approached me with the question: 'Peter, did you read that somewhere, or did you think up that answer spontaneously?'

I hesitated a moment and then resorted to a white lie: 'Sir, I read it somewhere.'

The class breathed a sigh of relief.

CHAPTER THREE

THE BEGINNINGS OF A
RESEARCH SCIENTIST

In 1933, a warrant for the arrest of Albert Einstein was issued by the Gestapo because, as a German Jew, he had been warning foreign countries about the new Nazi regime. He emigrated to the United States and lived a retired life in a small university town until his death in 1955. Hardly anybody there was interested in his theories of relativity, and in Germany the theories were entirely censored. When I was a young man in the 1950s, Einstein had not yet attained the status he enjoys today of being the greatest physicist of the 20th century. His name was almost unknown then. Only in the last 20 years has his life's work in physics acquired such major significance, finding application in two different areas of science – particle physics and astrophysics. These subjects will be discussed later in connection with the Big Bang theory.

One day I came across a small book by Albert Einstein and Leopold Infeld, *The Evolution of Physics*. I was fascinated by the idea of the speed of light. Einstein was the first to realize that this was a natural constant the value of which never changes. Even if a lamp from which light was emitted at the speed of light were to be fixed to the front of a rocket that was itself moving through space at high speed, the speed of the light beam would remain constant relative to the source of light. This speed measures almost exactly 300,000 km per second (186,283 miles per second).

Scientists distinguish between the mathematical constants

invented by man and natural constants. The mathematical constants, for instance, include the geometrical number (π = 3.141... and Euler's number e = 2.718... Strangely enough, the whole edifice of physics is based on these 'invented' numbers. Physicists do not question the absolute value of natural constants but are eager to debate such questions as 'How would it be if, for example, the speed of light or the gravitation constant had different values?' Mathematical constants are on the other hand not obtained through measurements but 'discovered' by calculation, and are therefore generally not open to discussion. I could hardly have guessed then that I would later be able to prove that mathematical constants are also natural constants. They were therefore not invented, just discovered, by man.

I asked myself what else would change if light were to travel at a different speed – say, 500,000 kilometres per second (310,685 miles per second). Basically, nothing essential to physics or the theory of relativity would seem to change because we could just as easily take a new value for the speed of light as the value normally given. However, the essence of a natural constant is to be found precisely in the fact that it can be expressed with a single, unchangeable, numerical value. Because the speed of light is specified in the decimal system with the dimensions of distance (kilometres or miles) and time (seconds), this value would seem to be arbitrary. And in a different numerical system and in other units of measurement the value would in fact be different. This line of reasoning is wrong. For the absolute quantitative value relative to universal reality nothing at all would change. We are only confusing the situation when we express the speed of light in terms of a symbol – in this case c.

The essence of the speed of light, of this natural constant, is to be found in its numerical value. This must simply involve a number – in the simplest case a one, a three, or some other *rational* number, but possibly also an *irrational* or a *transcendental* number (the three types of numbers are discussed later).

No other subject in modern physics has been debated at such length as the theory of relativity. Most of it has been pure repetition. In actual fact, nobody knows why only light can travel at that particular speed whereas an object – whether it be an atom or a rocket – cannot be accelerated to the speed of light. We are currently being bombarded with fairytales of speeds greater than the speed of light, recounted by charlatans who completely distort Einstein's work.

Back then I had already come to the conclusion that our ideas of space and time were not correct. Some years later I learned that the scientist Hendrik A Lorentz – who Einstein himself regarded as the greatest living physicist – had actually warned explicitly on his deathbed that the theory of relativity had to be wrong, although Einstein's reasoning was entirely correct and although the relativity effect could be unmistakably demonstrated through physical experiment. That satisfied me. Nothing can be correct and false at the same time. When I have discovered a problem, I become sceptical. But if a second person also recognizes it, the situation can no longer be ignored. For the speed of light to be a natural constant, this constant must have a numerical value. The task of finding such a value was a daunting one indeed.

In 1906 Albert Einstein expressed in an equation the relationship between energy E and mass m. Energy in this case refers to electromagnetic energy – for example, light and microwave energy. The two basic constituents of the universe, energy and material mass, are thus linked in the equation

$$E = m\ c^2$$

to the two other basic fundamental elements, space and time. The term c corresponds to a speed – that is, distance over time – and c^2 stands for the square of the speed of light. The layman will find it difficult to imagine anything like the square of the speed of light. Physicists are not able to imagine what it is like either. This formula comes tripping off their lips so easily because it is the result of a calculation. Because the calculation says that it is so, it is simply accepted.

With this equation Einstein uncovered one of nature's impenetrable puzzles, which I would like to illustrate here.

Take two buckets and let them float in a lake at some distance from each other. Then begin pressing one of the buckets up and down in the water. A circular wave immediately forms and spreads from the centre of the moving bucket. When this wave

27

reaches the second bucket, it will begin also to move up and down at the same rate. Now imagine that the medium of water is no longer there. We would then be unable to transfer energy from one bucket to the other. But if we take the oscillating electrons in the light emitted by a candle or a lamp instead of the waves spreading from a bucket, the experiment would work again and there would be no need for anything in the middle except empty space. This experiment would now not involve the emission of water waves but of electromagnetic waves.

The physicists at the time were convinced that the transmission of electromagnetic energy required a medium for the wave. They called this medium the *ether*. Einstein was the first to claim that the transmission of electromagnetic waves did not require any medium. Space itself would be the medium. Einstein realised that there was no need for matter to be present in the gap between transmitter and receiver, whereas in the case of energy passing between the two buckets a medium – water – was needed. After Einstein had disputed the assistance of the ether as a medium of transmission, a theory had to be found to explain how the wave could be transmitted – for a wave cannot oscillate in nothing. Could it be that space itself possesses an invisible structure imperceptible by us, an invisible grid structure, with the help of which electromagnetic energy can be transmitted? Space must in that case be more than just nothing. This meant that our understanding of space had to be wrong.

In 1945, the world learned that Einstein's formula could be 'utilised': the explosive power of the atom bomb was based on this equation. A few grams of matter were transformed into an enormous amount of electromagnetic energy precisely because the square of the speed of light is arithmetically a very large number. But this great 'success' also exploded any hopes of asking why this occurred.

The absolute numerical value of the speed of light which I was pursuing with ever-increasing intensity had to be connected in some way with the nature of empty space itself, which ever since Einstein had taken the place of the ether. My proposal was for the first time to suggest an essential identity between number and space – which should not be confused with the loose relationship between space and number used in geometry by mathematicians.

Space has a three-fold, qualitatively identical extension –

length
width
height

the relative perspectives of which can perhaps best be conceptualized if the reader brings to the mind's eye the dimensions of a familiar room.

Shortly after Einstein's relativity theories appeared, the idea of expanding the concept of space by a further dimension quickly emerged. This did not involve a fourth extension in space, just a single additional dimension in the form of time.

And it is on this that my criticism came to bear. Time, like space, has a three-fold nature: it is made up of

past
present
future

At that time I did not know that the physicists' notion of time as a single dimension was based on the philosophy of Immanuel Kant[1] which was in turn based on the scientific approach of Newton. I was confronted with a problem, whereas for physicists the problem had long been considered solved. It is a curious thing that complex mathematical equations in physics can indeed be disentangled when the three dimensions of space are linked with time to form a four-dimensional space-time structure. Because both space and time are notions involving infinity and both are three-fold phenomena, I began to consider the concept of number. In the course of my research I entered a fascinating world which by virtue of my knowledge of chemistry did not involve that mysticism surrounding numbers so scorned by mathematicians. Instead it involved a firm correlation between numbers and our material world.

As we have already seen, every atom consists of one atomic nucleus and a shell of electrons that may be considered to orbit around the tiny centre. The nucleus consists of protons and neutrons, the number of which can be established by sophisticated measuring equipment. Because the protons are electrically positive and the electrons in the electron cloud have a negative charge, they generally occur in the same number.

29

The most simple element consists of atoms with a nucleus containing only one proton and thus with one electron in orbit around the nucleus. This element is hydrogen, and is given the atomic number 1. The element with the atomic number 2 has two protons and thus also two electrons; we call this element helium. The sequence continues until element 83, which is bismuth and has 83 protons and 83 electrons. For historical reasons, scientists refer to the various elements by their names and not by their respective atomic numbers, although that would be entirely sufficient to identify them.

The number system of the elements is so simple that I am surprised that every child doing maths at school is not introduced to it. This simple regularity with its practical relevance would serve as an ideal introduction to the laws of mathematics while at the same time familiarizing the children with the fundamentals of the material world.

The stable elements in the periodic system are therefore made up of the number series of 1, 2, 3 … 83.

There is, however, a problem here of which chemists and physicists are generally not aware: for some strange reason two elements do not exist – the elements with the atomic numbers 43 and 61. They also do not exist outside this planet, at least not anywhere in the solar system – a fact only recognized during my youth.

But because scientists have been able to synthesize both elements artificially in modern nuclear reactors, they have both been given names, even though they very quickly degrade into other elements. They have therefore long been mentioned in textbooks on chemistry and physics. When I was young I too fell into the trap of believing that they existed in reality because they had been artificially listed alongside the natural elements. Only because I continued studying nuclear chemistry and physics after I had completed my chemistry studies did I come to a full realization of the absence of the two elements as a fact.

The discovery proved to be a key to the door leading to nature's secret.

For some reason, scientists do not seem to worry that two members of the list of stable elements are, in fact, unstable.

If any student should chance to enquire at a lecture why elements 43 and 61, technetium and promethium, do not exist in nature, the professor would probably reply: 'Because they are unstable.'

In this way the questioning student would look stupid and not the professor.[2]

The atomic nucleus also contains, in addition to its protons, neutron particles – that is, particles with a neutral charge. This remained undiscovered until 1932. The beryllium nucleus, for example, has four protons and five neutrons. Four and five together gives the so-called atomic weight 9. Unfortunately, this type of description is very confusing as atomic number and atomic weight are designated in the same way: as simple numbers. Before 1932 nobody knew why the atomic number 4 and the atomic weight 9 did not match.

Bismuth, the last stable element, has an atomic weight of 209, although it has the atomic number 83. If you subtract the number of protons (83) from the number 209 (the atomic weight), you get 126. That is the exact number of neutrons in the bismuth atom. It should be clearly emphasized at this point that nobody in the world knows why there should be precisely 126 neutrons and not 127 or 125.

This particular form is referred to as bismuth isotope 209, because there are also other bismuth nuclei that have different numbers of neutrons. Such nuclei are, however, unstable and degrade or 'decay' into atomic nuclei with other atomic numbers. They are then no longer atoms of bismuth. The process of decay is called radioactivity. Because there is only one stable bismuth isotope, it is classed among the pure isotopes as are all other elements with only one stable isotope.

There are also elements with several stable atomic forms. One example is element number 8, oxygen, which has three forms of atom with different neutron-proton ratios: one isotope with 8 neutrons and atomic weight 16; one with 9 neutrons and atomic weight 17; and a third with 10 neutrons and atomic weight 18. All of these go under the name oxygen.

Neither schools or universities seem to be capable of communicating this elementary knowledge in an understandable way. But we may liken an element with isotopes to a family with children. No matter how many children there are, the family remains the family. So an element remains that element no matter how many isotopes it has.

Yet although greater numbers of children in a family are not unknown, one element can have an absolute maximum of ten isotopes.

Nobody knows why this is so. It is perhaps characteristic that scarcely any physicist or chemist with the title of doctor has any knowledge of this limit of ten. It is necessary to point out that we are deliberately kept in the dark about the basic fact that there can be no more than ten isotopes because the number ten appears a bit too mystical for some people in high places.

The elements, after all, occur with a maximum number of isotopes the same as we have fingers on our hands. Because the number of fingers we have is considered to be a coincidence, the experts are afraid of also having to describe the number of isotopes as a coincidence. Natural processes are held to be governed by coincidence, but natural laws such as isotope formation can never be mere chance.

The question 'Why?' is strictly forbidden in physics. In answering such a simple question the framework of our 'consummate knowledge' would be immediately seen to be less than solid. We might then begin to ask such questions as why element 83 is the last stable element.

No further elements should really exist after element 83, for all of their atoms are so radioactive that they ought to have disappeared soon after our planet was formed. For some reason unknown to us, two elements beyond element 83 – those with the atomic numbers 90 (thorium) and 92 (uranium) – have a life of thousands of millions of years. Large quantities of these two elements still remain since their creation. They were analysed in the last century and have since been synthesized in a pure chemical state. Both elements are constantly decaying and by doing so they themselves provide elements 91, 89, 88, 87, 86, 85 and 84.

To Marie and Pierre Curie tribute must be paid for being the first to isolate tiny amounts of elements 84 (polonium) and 88 (radium). But an unequivocal statement that stable elements exist only up to element 83, and that beyond these a second class of elements exists that are derived from elements 92 and 90 and are referred to as naturally radioactive – such a clear statement could not be made at the time.

Even before the end of the Second World War a way had been

32

Table 1. The 81 stable chemical elements

Atomic number	Name	Chemical symbol	Number of isotopes	Atomic number	Name	Chemical symbol	Number of isotopes
1	**Hydrogen**	**H**	**2**	(43	Technetium	Tc	–)
2	**Helium**	**He**	**2**	44	Ruthenium	Ru	7
3	**Lithium**	**Li**	**2**	45	Rhodium	Rh	1
4	**Beryllium**	**Be**	**1**	46	Palladium	Pd	6
5	**Boron**	**B**	**2**	47	Silver	Ag	2
6	**Carbon**	**C**	**2+1**	48	Cadmium	Cd	8
7	**Nitrogen**	**N**	**2**	49	**Indium**	**In**	**2**
8	**Oxygen**	**O**	**3**	50	**Tin**	**Sn**	**10**
9	**Fluorine**	**F**	**1**	51	**Antimony**	**Sb**	**2**
10	**Neon**	**Ne**	**3**	52	**Tellurium**	**Te**	**8**
11	**Sodium**	**Na**	**1**	53	**Iodine**	**I**	**1**
12	**Magnesium**	**Mg**	**3**	54	**Xenon**	**Xe**	**9**
13	**Aluminium**	**Al**	**1**	55	**Caesium**	**Cs**	**1**
14	**Silicon**	**Si**	**3**	56	**Barium**	**Ba**	**7**
15	**Phosphorus**	**P**	**1**	57	Lanthanum	La	2
16	**Sulphur**	**S**	**4**	58	Cerium	Ce	4
17	**Chlorine**	**Cl**	**2**	59	Praseodymium	Pr	1
18	**Argon**	**Ar**	**3**	60	Neodymium	Nd	7
19	**Potassium**	**K**	**3**	(61	Promethium	Pm	–)
20	**Calcium**	**Ca**	**6**	62	Samarium	Sm	7
21	Scandium	Sc	1	63	Europium	Eu	2
22	Titanium	Ti	5	64	Gadolinium	Gd	7
23	Vanadium	V	2	65	Terbium	Tb	1
24	Chromium	Cr	4	66	Dysprosium	Dy	7
25	Manganese	Mn	1	67	Holmium	Ho	1
26	Iron	Fe	4	68	Erbium	Er	6
27	Cobalt	Co	1	69	Thulium	Tm	1
28	Nickel	Ni	5	70	Ytterbium	Yb	7
29	Copper	Cu	2	71	Lutetium	Lu	2
30	Zinc	Zn	5	72	Hafnium	Hf	6
31	**Gallium**	**Ga**	**2**	73	Tantalum	Ta	2
32	**Germanium**	**Ge**	**5**	74	Tungsten	W	5
33	**Arsenic**	**As**	**1**	75	Rhenium	Re	2
34	**Selenium**	**Se**	**6**	76	Osmium	Os	7
35	**Bromine**	**Br**	**2**	77	Iridium	Ir	2
36	**Krypton**	**Kr**	**6**	78	Platinum	Pt	6
37	**Rubidium**	**Rb**	**2**	79	Gold	Au	1
38	**Strontium**	**Sr**	**4**	80	Mercury	Hg	7
39	Yttrium	Y	1	81	**Thallium**	**Tl**	**2**
40	Zirconium	Zr	5	82	**Lead**	**Pb**	**4**
41	Niobium	Nb	1	83	**Bismuth**	**Bi**	**1**
42	Molybdenum	Mo	7				

Elements of the main groups are in bold type, elements of the sub-groups are in normal type. The elements 43 and 61 are not stable and do not occur in nature.

found to isolate the artificial elements 93 and 94 from element 92, and even higher elements were also soon discovered. They also involved volumes large enough to be visible for the first time. However, no isotope of these elements proved to be stable, which means that any elements of this type disappeared very soon after the creation of the solar system. These constitute the third form of elements. Such a division of the components of our universe into three categories was not recognized at the time. Such distinctions were well concealed. We now reckon on:

1) stable elements (1–83) [without 43 and 61]
2) naturally radioactive elements (84–92)
3) exclusively artificial elements (93–106)

Before the Second World War, students learned that there were elements up to atomic number 92 whereas today they have to learn that there are 106 elements. Such scientific superficiality is partly the result of the the vanity of scientists. For example, elements 104, 105 and 106 cannot be synthesized at all: the few atoms that have ever been created have disintegrated within fractions of a second.

Because of the modern obsession with attempts to discover new elements and coin names for them, the question why the new elements are increasingly unstable has been totally avoided. One consequence of this shortsightedness is the presentation of all 106 elements with their names in our textbooks and in the Periodic Table.[3] No problem is perceived in the fact that the list of stable elements contains two elements that are, in fact, unstable and thus have no isotopes.

In view of this, it is clear that the two unstable elements should be omitted from this group of 83. That would then give us a final number of 81 stable elements.

In 1981 the paperback German edition of Isaac Asimov's *Book of Facts* appeared. The author, the world-famous writer and chemist, reports on page 93 that 'There are only 81 stable elements,' and that all other elements are radioactive. Unfortunately, he did not take his remarkable discovery to its logical conclusion.

The table of the 81 elements on page 33 presents any reader wishing to pursue this matter further with an illustration of the subject. These details are unfortunately still not found in ordinary chemistry and physics books.

The three-fold nature of the building-blocks of the universe was the most important discovery of my youth. Such knowledge cannot be acquired by reading. I attained this insight through my involvement with the problem of radioactivity. The Curies and a host of other researchers had discovered that the elements 90 and 92 break up through *three* radioactive decay series into the *three* stable isotopes of lead **206**, **207** and **208**, and that this process takes place by the release of radiation which is also of *three* types,

alpha rays
beta rays
gamma rays

In that it was established in the 1930s that all elements are composed of *three* types of elementary particles – protons, neutrons, electrons – it was certainly high time to consider this apparent preponderance of threesomes. Such a scientific consideration never took place.

It gradually became clear to me just how many unresolved questions there are when one looks closely into chemistry, whereas all the books report only the great successes. But at that time I was looking forward to studying chemistry and did not want to spoil the pleasure of anticipation.

It had been intended that I try to find a place at the chemistry faculty of Cologne University and that my brother Paul with his intermediate certificate and his apprenticeship in engineering would study mechanical engineering at the college of engineering, also in Cologne. But for that it would be necessary for him to come to grips with mathematics, physics and chemistry. I would have to give him coaching on a daily basis. How would he ever be able to manage his studies? Why were my brother and I so completely different? The question worried me.

Some weeks before the final examination I had to prepare a handwritten curriculum vitae for the school. Instead of dashing off two pages with all the necessary information, I sat at home paralysed with the problem of writing about who I was and what I intended to do with my life. What finally emerged after many attempts was a strange concoction – the significance of

35

being born a twin, visionary proposals to improve the world, and the assertion that science knows nothing. As might have been expected, these declarations were not accepted. After several vain attempts, my class teacher personally dictated to me the sober and meaningless statement that was required.

After nine years at the secondary school, the day of the final oral examination finally arrived. Just as I went out through the main door into the yard before leaving the school forever, the director was also leaving. For him it was also his last day at the school. He would be, I knew, a pensioner from that day on.

'Mr Plichta, I wonder if you would mind accompanying me this last time across the yard to the bus-stop? You are the most remarkable pupil I have come across in my whole career as a teacher. You have been one of the wildest pupils the school has ever had, and I had you categorized as a young hooligan and a congenital rebel. I now believe I misjudged you. You are actually a boy of great sensitivity. You are also a deep thinker and very clever. I shouldn't be surprised if you turn into something fairly special when you grow up. I feel I should give you something very important to take with you on your way. If you ever have self-doubts, remember my words – remember how I rated you today. Believe in yourself.'

He then gave me his hand. I was very moved.

NOTES
1 As stated in Kant, Immanuel, *Critique of Pure Reason*, p 47: time 'has only one dimension: different times are not simultaneous but subsequent to each other (just as different spaces are not subsequent to each other but simultaneous).'
2 In the Deutsches Museum in Munich, the visitor can observe all the elements of the Periodic Table in sealed test tubes. When a certain button is pressed on an electric board, a lamp lights under the respective element. The tubes for elements 43 and 61 are empty. These artificially synthesized elements are radioactive and may therefore not be placed close to the unsuspecting public. By including empty test tubes instead of omitting the tubes entirely, a 'satisfactory solution' to the problem has been found.
3 Recently the isolation of elements 107 to 111 by bombarding stable elements with heavy ions has been described as their 'preparation'. The life expectancy of such individual atoms is no longer than one thousandth of a second.

CHAPTER FOUR

NUMBER AND PLAN

I matriculated at the University of Cologne during the summer semester of 1959. Paul was forced to interrupt his studies after only one semester and instead took up an apprenticeship as a shipping clerk. He used to spend his weekends in an ambulance on the highways of Germany working for the St John Ambulance Brigade. He wore a khaki-coloured uniform with peaked cap and shoulder bag bearing a large eight-pointed St John's cross. This cross had a strange effect on me – as if this geometric pattern reminded me of something, a feeling of *déja vú*. Paul himself was not interested in the cross at all. He was dreaming of a medical career at that time.

That was the summer I met Helga Ring. She was an extremely striking girl, 16 years old, and attending secondary school. I soon noticed the light bronze sheen of her skin. In reply to my enquiry she told me that she had inherited this beautiful colour from her father. When I then asked what her father's profession was, she answered, 'A chemist'.

I was delighted. I then asked her rather shyly if she would also like to study chemistry. After all, I had for so long been looking for a girlfriend who could not only share my life but also my passion for chemical formulae.

'Perhaps,' she replied.

I was euphoric. I asked what her father did.

'He is dead. He died of an unknown muscular disease.' Apparently her father, an active sportsman, had first lost all feeling in one of his legs. Later the paralysis spread to the other leg, and soon the arms were also affected. Helga related how her mother had had to give her husband artificial respiration during the heavy air raids on Berlin in 1945 as his lungs were failing day by day.

At that moment, for the first time in my 19 years, I had a vision. I heard my own voice say to her urgently, 'Be careful you don't die of lung failure just as your father did.'

Later I had, with horror, to witness how this young girl too died of lung failure. I could have bitten off my tongue because of the words I had said. But I later realized that Helga had not understood the full meaning of my words. We were married a few years later.

The practical part of my chemistry studies involved chemical analysis by boiling. The students would place their white porcelain pestle and mortars in front of the dispensing bay, and would receive the bowls back the following day half-filled with a mixture of coloured salts. Each analysis process thereafter would increase the number of potential elements in the mixture.

The student nevertheless never got to know more than half of all the elements. He only learned about those elements that were relevant to the purposes of the professors and for industry. It is considered happily beneficial that the universe contains silver and uranium, silicon compounds with oxygen, and sugars consisting of the elements carbon, oxygen and hydrogen. These can be exploited in various ways. With such a utilitarian attitude to matter, the student of chemistry or physics is soon of the opinion that such elements as indium, holmium or rhenium are completely useless. But it surely cannot be expected that the Big Bang happened only to produce matter that is useful – universal garbage has to exist too!

At the end of the usual period at university, the student is not even capable of answering the question of how many stable elements there are. He or she has become accustomed to throwing the three types of elements into one and the same pot. And this despite the fact that the three-fold form of matter occurs so frequently in nature.

At normal temperature all 81 stable elements are either **solid (eg sulphur), liquid (eg mercury)** or **gas (eg nitrogen)**.

The elements of the main groups in the periodic system are also categorized in three groups according to their material characteristics and chemical and physical behaviour:

non-metallic (eg oxygen)
metalloid (eg arsenic)
metallic (eg lead)

The elements of the subgroups are always metals. The methods of combination by which the elements bond with each other are also of three kinds and are strictly divided into

ionic bonds (eg common salt)
atomic bonds (eg methane)
metallic bonds (eg brass)

The triple nature of chemical bonding is what is important here, not any specialist knowledge of the variety of such compounds.

The abundance of 'unimportant' elements has a disorienting effect on the student of chemistry, and most are relieved to be able to concentrate on organic substances for their graduate studies. Organic chemistry is concerned only with compounds of carbon and a limited number of other elements.

There is again a strict three-fold division in organic chemistry. Carbon can form three types of bonds:

simple bonds
double bonds
triple bonds

In all the universe there are only three elements capable of forming these three types of bonds:

carbon
nitrogen
oxygen

For years I had been looking forward to meeting other students with the same love for chemistry as I had. But I found none at the university. Some were much more knowledgeable than I, but when I began to sound them and ask them about what they planned to do with this knowledge, I discovered that none of them could imaging doing anything other than what their predecessors had done. Chemists just do not consider it their task to go looking for answers to such questions as why elements exist in the first place, or what the meaning hidden behind the system is. But whose task is it then?

Because biochemistry is not part of a chemistry student's training, scarcely any of them would ever venture into such an area. Today biochemistry has attained such a status that it has been promoted to an independent field of study.

The first lecture I went to was attended by only three other students, mostly biologists. A big, fat man shot into the auditorium and commenced his lecture for all the world like a state prosecutor, with his arms widely gesticulating for dramatic effect.

'Just as the entire edifice of literature is constructed out of 24 different letters, just as Goethe's *Faust* is composed of the same 24 characters,[1] the miracle of life is also made up of 24 different amino acids,' he declared.

The students around me all had their heads down, busy writing word for word what the professor was saying. I, however, was seized by an excitement I had never experienced before. Could it be that the two corresponding numbers – in both cases 24 – that were used by the professor as a mnemonic and for rhetoric embellishment, were in fact no coincidence at all? The man in front of us had made a statement without for a moment imagining just how explosive his statement was. His words had triggered off a bomb inside my head.

I was perfectly aware of the enormous consequences of this assumption. Suppressing my natural shyness, when the lecture had ended I went straight to the few good chemistry students in my semester and started up a discussion on this subject. It did not last very long.

'Plichta, the number of letters or of amino acids is completely arbitrary. How could amino acids have any connection with letters? It's all total coincidence. And in any case nothing matters a damn anyway.'

Amino acids are building-blocks, chemical combinations out of which protein is composed. Protein in turn is the substance from which all living matter is made. The spatial structure of proteins requires – in contrast to normal chemical compounds – that they be described with the terms 'left' and 'right': analogous to the left and right hand.

This was nothing new to me at that time. But the question now was why life should be linked to one particular chemical bond and why to one particular number of compounds. The favourable chemical structure of the amino acids tended to prevent this question from being asked in the first place.

The first thing I discovered was that there were not 24 amino acids at all, but precisely 20. The professor in his academic omnipotence had simply added an extra four. In fairness, scientists in 1959 were still generally unaware that the proteins that make up everything from bacteria, which have no cellular body, to mammals are composed of only 20 amino acids. This is also true for all types of vegetation from green algae to flowers. The endlessly recurring objection that there are further amino acids – for example in penicillin, which has the composition of fungus (no protein!) – may furnish proof of some knowledge in organic chemistry but shows useful ignorance of the basic rules of biology (genetics). We can dismiss the reports that crop up in specialist literature every now and again relating to so-called clockwise-turning amino acids in certain anaerobic micro-organisms that live on hydrogen sulphide.

One other thing about these amino acids I found particularly intriguing. They are made up of 19 left-oriented amino acids (the right-oriented amino acids do not occur in nature but can be synthesized in the laboratory). In addition there is one amino acid that has no optical centre and that can therefore be said to have both a left and right orientation. The professor of biology had thus brought me via the number 24 to the number 19. I could not have known at the time the significance of the number 24.

Life is therefore coded with 19 left-oriented amino acids, and *Faust* is written using 19 consonants as well as the five vowels.[2] Consonants are the basic building-blocks of all human language. We shall be taking a look at consonants later.

When I was 19 years old I was confronted with a question that requires an answer: did everything take place by coincidence or plan? *Tertium non datur* – there is no third option. There was no visible solution to the problem for the time being.

Amino acids are part of chemistry just as the numbers 1 and 19 are part of mathematics. This pointed the way for me. The number 19 is a prime number. The definition of prime numbers is that each is divisible only by the number 1 and the number itself.

This was convincing enough for me. I became fascinated by a small mental experiment. I imagined that God had given me as chemist and engineer the task of constructing beings with consciousness of self from those elements that must by necessity exist in the universe. These beings would therefore have to be equipped with language, because only those who can speak are also able to think cognitively. I would make use of a construction plan. For the body I would take a certain number of chemical components. This number would not be arbitrary – on the contrary, it would have to be precisely defined. What could be used to establish this number? I would select those numbers that constitute the foundation of all mathematics: prime numbers.

The prime numbers contain a very profound secret that mathematicians have never been able to solve. Was this the area in which my life's work was to be found?

A few years later I came across the number 19 for the third time. While I was studying physical chemistry I heard a professor say something during a lecture without his being aware of the deeper meaning of what he said. He pointed out that the total number of pure isotopes in all the stable elements is exactly 20. I have saved his lecture notes as evidence. Such references to mysterious correlations would later be barred from all discussion in universities. The professor described it as a very peculiar thing (while at the same time congratulating himself on his powers of observation) that of these 20 pure isotopes, the lowest element, beryllium, has the even atomic number 4, and that this is followed by the elements with the atomic numbers 9, 11, 13, 15, 21, 25, 27, 33, 39, 41, 45, 53, 55, 59, 65, 67, 69, 79, and 83.

You can see at a glance that there are 19 pure isotopes with uneven atomic numbers.

I now knew that the same number sequence occurs in both biochemistry and nuclear chemistry:

1 + 19 amino acids
and
1 + 19 pure isotopes

But in my self-appointed assignment as 'constructor' of life forms I had in point of fact overlooked something. The building-blocks with which I was planning to make these beings were chemical compounds. But they themselves, of course, consisted of even smaller units – chemical elements. Because I wanted to choose only one and the same construction plan for the entire task, the point raised to my attention by the physicist was indeed utterly relevant.

Why had this correspondence between the building-blocks of life and the building-blocks of matter not been noticed by anyone before? Well, nuclear chemists deal with isotopes and biochemists deal with amino acids. Both types of 'chemists' undergo totally different training to meet the needs of their respective fields. At the same time the university syllabus for ordinary chemists does not include either biochemistry or nuclear chemistry. It is as simple as that.

It was at that point that I realized I would later also have to study nuclear chemistry and biochemistry. I was, however, confident that I would be able to avoid studying mathematics. One thing was certain in any case: if my suspicions turned out to be well-founded, it would mean a major upheaval in our concept of the world.

Physical chemistry is an obligatory subject for every student of chemistry. Because most chemists are not interested in physics and loathe mathematics, the majority of young chemists have a horror of the subject. The special domain of physical chemistry is thermodynamics, because many chemical processes produce heat. The extremely complex mathematical calculations that relate to this science were already complete at the end of the 19th century, a time at which science was dominated by an attitude similar to the one prevailing today: we know everything that is to be known. Max Planck had no inhibitions in reporting that a famous professor of physics had tried to discourage him from studying with the remark that no more important discoveries were left to be made.

Achievements in the field of thermodynamics were in fact among the most outstanding and impressive advances made by humankind in the 19th century. Albert Einstein himself was so impressed by them that he maintained that even if contemporary physics was ever replaced by a new form of physics in the future, one aspect of the 'old' physics would certainly survive – the laws of thermodynamics. By this, Einstein meant the three pillars of physical chemistry – the first, second and third laws of thermodynamics. He also went into more detail about how he could conceive the foundation of such a new physics: it would be based on numbers!

I was fascinated. When I read this for the first time I was quite sure that this answer was the work of genius. But one thing still puzzled me. Why did he not suspect a deeper meaning for thermodynamics?

The three laws of thermodynamics are purely empirical, being arrived at through experience. The veritable jungle of mathematical formulas required to establish the laws and to prove them also causes the curious to become disheartened. At this level even greater complexity is possible, and this was in blatant contradiction to my quest for simplicity.

The first two laws of thermodynamics preclude the existence of a *perpetuum mobile*: they state that energy is always lost when undergoing change or use. The third law says that at the lowest possible temperature of –273.2°C, or absolute zero, no more movement of atoms takes place and the value for entropy[3] is thus zero.

Now the number 273.2 had interested me ever since my time at school. The experiments of Gay-Lussac proved that gases expand and contract by 1/273.2 of their volume for every degree of heating or cooling. I was intrigued that a certain number is taken as a value for one phenomenon and its precise reciprocal value taken for another, without causing even one physicist in the whole world to lose a minute's sleep. When the measure of temperature was established at 0°C for the freezing point of water and 100° for its boiling point, the standard temperature was simply fixed in the decimal system because that lends itself easily to calculation. Water was chosen because melting ice always shows a constant temperature. This arbitrary choice gave me food for thought. Temperature is very difficult to explain in physical terms. No steam really has a uniform temperature of 100°C; that only corresponds to a value for the mean speed of the gas molecules.

What does a thermometer really measure? The shielded mercury is bombarded by the gas molecules. Most of the molecules fly at a speed corresponding to a temperature of approximately 100°C, although many molecules are much colder or much warmer. A volume of gas molecules in which all have a temperature of 100°C does not exist. The mercury accordingly registers a comparatively false value of 100°C. We define the heat content of a gas as the movement of its molecules. Movement is change of position in space. The same rule that forces an electromagnetic wave to maintain a particular speed also surrounds every gas molecule. We do not know what space really means, however. We therefore also know nothing about the true nature of temperature and heat, despite the fact that our kettles and boilers function perfectly.

Another approach also leads to the same result. The three forms in which matter exists at any one time – **solid**, **liquid**, or **gas** – depend on pressure and temperature. All physical dimensions can be reduced to three basic dimensions – **length (or distance)**, **mass**, and **time** – of which the standard units until superseded by those of the SI systems introduced by C F Gauss were generally cited as the **centimetre**, the **gram**, and the **second**.

Even the notion of electric charge, which is very difficult to comprehend, can be reduced to basic mechanical dimensions.

I infer from this trinity of basic dimensions and the notion of mechanical movement that temperature is itself not a basic dimension. I would describe it as a state of which the true nature will remain unknown to us as long as we do not understand what space really is.

We received good news from Paul. He had passed his examinations as a commercial clerk and his company now wanted to offer him a post with a salary of around $150 a month. Paul and I sat down in my little room and I told him he should not even consider accepting such an offer.

He was already going steady with a girl at the time, as was I. His girlfriend, who wanted to study medicine – a subject that was quite beyond him at that time – came from a family of industrialists, and her mother was a billionaire. The situation haunted him like a nightmare: he was reduced to tremors by the thought that her family would not hear of a commercial clerk as husband for their daughter.

On the other hand, I was delighted by this new Peter and Paul constellation. His girlfriend would one day not only be a shareholder in some firm, she would be shareholder in a giant chemical corporation.

I told him that the family into which he hoped to marry would have nothing against him provided the girl truly loved him. High-flying adventurers, imposters and tricksters were generally accepted, as were racing drivers and princes. Nonetheless, an honest young man who worked for a furniture transport company for DM400 a month would never be accepted.

'Is there anything I can do to give myself a better chance?' he asked soulfully.

'I shall organize another job for you or get you back into studying again.'

One week later, on 17 September 1963, Paul came to me and told me that he would now have to make the decision. I believed I had the solution but I had not thought it right through at this stage.

Paul went to talk to our ailing father, who immediately called me into the living-room.

'Paul says that a final decision must be made now. He says that you have got a job for him. But you haven't got one, have you?'

'I do have a job for him,' I heard myself reply. At the same time I felt as if I had been touched by an icy breath. My father seemed somehow to have read what was in my mind. He looked at me with a strange sense of premonition.

'But even if you could do something for Paul, do you really believe that such a family would accept him as one of their own?'

'You have always underestimated Paul', I replied. 'You have always regarded as stupidity and laziness anything that was not outward industry and intelligence. But marriages are made according to other rules.'

'Just imagine what might have happened if you had been the one to meet this girl!'

I wasn't having that. 'The founders of the firm knew something about chemistry, but that has all been lost on the grandchildren and great-grandchildren. They don't even know what chemistry is. They are only interested in money and power. I have great plans to do with chemistry. Better for me to remain in the background for the time being. Paul can play the Trojan horse, but Peter will be sitting inside the horse!'

I saw my very ill father suddenly overcome with exhaustion: he looked drawn and pale. But then his face began to relax and I knew he had understood me.

Two hours later my father was dead and I had taken over the 'leadership' of the Plichta family.

At the funeral, the marketing director of the Canadian steel corporation for which my father had been working ever since he had left the civil service took me to one side.

'Mr Plichta, your father was very much respected in our firm. I would now like to present you with this sum of money for your mother.'

He drew his wallet from his pocket and took out a cheque from his company. I took it in my hand and read the amount. It was a very high sum.

'I am sure my mother would be very grateful for such a kindly gesture. But she is already well looked after and does not actually need the money.' And so saying, I gave him back the cheque. The director returned it to his wallet. He then looked at me for a while before asking the question I had been hoping to hear.

'Can I do anything at all for you?'

'Could you possibly find a position for my brother in your European headquarters in Switzerland? He has an intermediate school certificate, some technical training and a completed commercial apprenticeship.'

'Is your brother like you?'

I told him that he was.

'Then he's got the job.'

NOTES

1 C and k, and f and v have the same pronunciation in German, and count as one letter each. The number of letters in the alphabet is thus effectively reduced to 24 (19 consonants and 5 vowels).

2 The larynx functions like a wind instrument. Air from the lungs is compressed by the vocal cords and we thus generate the sounds called vowels. Consonants on the other hand are generated by the action of three oral organs, lips, teeth and tongue.

3 A chemical reaction has three results: the final product, heat, and entropy. An example will illustrate the notion of entropy: when a small amount of carbon is burned, the resulting carbon dioxide molecules spread through the room. If one wanted to reverse this reaction, all molecules would have first to be returned to the place where they started. And this is impossible.

CHAPTER FIVE

SPACE AND THE RIDDLE

For the first time in my life I had a secure income – a pension for the orphan of a civil servant. Until then I had financed my studies by odd jobs. I could now buy everything I required: a good bed and a desk with a swivel chair. Our house was no longer the scene of constant scraping and bickering over what we could afford. I had now found the peace I needed to study.

One morning I woke up in a complete daze. I sat on the edge of the bed and tried to get a grip of myself. Suddenly the dream from which I had just awoken came back to me like a stroke of lightning.

A man dressed in old-fashioned clothes was sitting in Stockholm in a great hall. He was to receive the Nobel Prize. A long time previously he had received three Nobel Prizes at the same time – the prizes for chemistry, physics and medicine. Now he had just returned from a long trip to our neighbouring stars. Two people had accompanied him but he had returned alone. He was being awarded the Nobel Prize once more because this journey had conclusively proved the accuracy of his earlier scientific theories. While he sat there listening to the conventional speeches given at such a ceremony, he saw as in a film the course of his whole life pass before him once more.

As a young man, he had been a passionate engineer in the spheres of rocket fuel and space technology. At first his genius had not been recognized at all. He chose a roundabout way to reach his goal. He hoped to discover the construction plan in which God had coded the universe. He was aware that this plan could not be discovered by someone experimenting in a laboratory. In order to realize his plans he had studied chemistry, physics and biology in succession, and delved deeply into the history and philosophy of these sciences. After many years of independent scientific research he had finally found the solution to the riddle of the universe.

He then got involved in a brilliant, uncompromising way in a brief and extremely bitter dispute with those who had been proclaiming for centuries that they had the sole rights to truth and knowledge, but who in reality were only trying to guard their sinecures. When that struggle had been won, he became the first person to be awarded three Nobel Prizes. He now had sufficient international recognition to be able to construct the rockets he knew humankind needed. He had developed two types of rocket – a disk craft and a space vehicle – as well as a new type of fuel. The space vehicle was very long, had a concave mirror at the rear end, and carried a rocket disk at its head which is used for landings on planets.

The funds necessary to implement his amazing ideas had been provided by the whole of humankind. He was now sitting once more in this hall.

His dream had now come to an end.

And my dream ended here, too.

I was dumbstruck. I knew that this dream had something to do with me. The search for the riddle of the universe in combination with rocket technology had been with me all my life. I also recognized the rocket disk – it was precisely the rocket that I had designed when I was 15. I had, however, not yet discovered anything about its fuel.

Throughout my childhood I had always been obsessed with two things – gunpowder and explosives, and futuristic novels. But even at the age of 15 I was convinced that space travel as conceived by the authors of science fiction novels could never be realized. Rockets fly in accordance with a certain mathematical equation which does not allow us to travel as in an aircraft from A to B and back without refilling. At that time I was quite convinced that space rockets – which at that time did not exist – were going to be constructed on the wrong principles.

I had read Wernher von Braun's books dealing with the complete theoretical calculation of flights to the Moon and to

Mars. I rejected his notions of using power modules based on hydrazine-nitric acid which demanded rockets of enormous size and expense. I considered the plan to be seriously defective in that multi-stage, liquid-fuelled rockets were to be used instead of much cheaper solid-propellant rockets. This appeared to me to be like helpless attempts by humanity to fight against the laws of nature. The rockets would either reach a speed of some 30,000 kilometres per hour or fall back onto the Earth. Either way, the whole expensive rocket would be seen no more. It is totally impractical to try to reach other planets with such rockets because braking and landing manoeuvres would require enormous amounts of fuel, as would the initial launching process.

Von Braun was always sure that space travel would become a reality as soon as the actual rockets could be built and fuelled on a satellite station in space. The enormous amounts of material required could perhaps be transported to the satellite station – as conceived by Sänger – by using two-stage rockets.

I became convinced that rockets in the shape of extended giant cigars, in which the whole weight has to be borne by a blast at one end, were wrongly conceived from the start. It would be better to build rockets in the form of aircraft which could utilize the lifting flow of the air surrounding it. I surmised that there was perhaps an ideal rocket shape and we had simply not yet found it.

I hit on the correct idea spontaneously as I looked at a drawing by Leonardo da Vinci – a sketch of a flying machine propelled by a large pedal-driven circular airscrew using human power.

The flying vehicle would have to be constructed as a disk with a ring of rotary blades for take-off, flying and landing operations close to gas-covered planets. This would avoid the high risk of explosion in long-distance rocket cylinders during take-off and landing. The rotary blades would be driven by four jet-turbines fitted inside the rigid disk, whose exhaust gases would be partly conducted into the external rotary ring where they would be used to rotate the propeller ring as well as lubricate the gas bearing. The remaining exhaust fumes would be released from the disk on the underside through a fixed funnel-shaped jet.

The exhaust fumes from an auxiliary liquid-fuelled rocket

engine could also be discharged through this jet to provide additional power for the jet-turbines, functioning like a water-jet blast on an exhaust burner.

Such a rocket would have many advantages. Should one or several engines fail during launch, the rocket would not crash because the rotary blade mechanism, the inner mechanism of which is held fixed by a countergear and does not move in relation to the rest of the vessel, can be steered just like a helicopter.

After the spaceship has left the atmosphere, only the rocket propulsion would remain running. When the rocket approached a planet with an atmosphere, the airscrew would allow the vessel to glide down slowly without consuming any fuel at all. Only in the final landing phase would the jet engines again be necessary. If the atmosphere was composed of ammonia or hydrocarbons, a liquid oxidant would suffice to power the turbines. If the atmosphere contained oxygen, liquid oxidation would be unnecessary.

I was overwhelmed by excitement and joy. Of course that was the answer. All the starting energy for a cigar-shaped rocket has to be generated by the rocket jets – a foolish waste of rocket fuel. The rocket must also be prevented from tilting to one side during launch. A disk-shaped rocket with a revolving blade rotor would be perfectly balanced by the torque of the rotor. Such a disk would not be subject to tilting caused by atmospheric disturbance. When the engines of a conventional rocket lose power or even fail completely, the whole rocket falls to the ground and explodes. My disk on the other hand would float back safely to Earth.

I prepared a technical drawing. In the evening I showed it to my father, to whom a whole series of patents had already been issued.

'Flying saucers are technically absurd,' he insisted.

But after I had explained to him in detail the advantages of this new type of flying craft he was suddenly gripped with excitement.

'Why that's fantastic!' he exclaimed and strode around the kitchen in excitement. This has to be registered at the patent office in Munich.'

Instead of being carried along by his excitement, I said to him, inspired by an inner voice, 'No, we can't patent the design. Our weak fuels would not be capable of lifting the disk like a single-stage rocket in one bound into space. You would have to put several disks on top of each other, and that would defeat the purpose. If the disk were to be accelerated horizontally by a rocket engine it would have limitless aerodynamic features. To patent it in Munich would enable the Americans and Russians to hijack the plan and use it for building aircraft to transport hydrogen bombs. A normal aircraft has to fly, but this disk would be able to stop and – like a fortress suspended in the sky – fire a full broadside. If it were to be attacked it could, in contrast to jet fighters, avoid the missiles by flying off into space.'

I saw that my father fully understood what I was saying. We looked intently into each other's eyes.

'Peter, do you believe that one day there will be fuels that burn at a higher temperature?'

With this question he voiced the fundamental problem of rocket engineering. Any new rocket design would have to be linked to a new fuel which would have to have better combustion characteristics than those known hitherto.

I listened in amazement to my own answer: 'Yes, father. I believe that in our system of elements there is an element that has the power to boost this new type of rocket into space like a single-stage craft.'

'Then go and find this fuel, and when you have found it have your two inventions patented together.'

I immediately realized how right he was. It was the only time in my life that I admired my father.

Naturally my ideas at that time could hardly be mature from a technical point of view. Another 40 years would pass before the patent for the disk and the fuel would be applied for and registered.

When I was 15 years old Leonardo's drawing had presented me with the idea for my rocket disk. Years later the third and fourth diary of the Renaissance genius were found in the Prado museum in Madrid. I was strangely moved when I learned that at the end of the fourth diary he had written a very special salutation in the language of the quattrocento and in mirror

53

writing:

Dear Reader, read me well
For it is only seldom that I return
to this Earth

L da V

At that time I still had no idea what the chemical composition of this fuel could be. I did not even know it would necessarily involve a compound of the elements silicon and hydrogen.

What could justify our desire to visit neighbouring stars? The efforts and costs required for such a venture are unimaginably great. And what could be discovered there? Columbus had returned form his discoveries with decoratively painted Central American 'Indians' and, of course, with gold.

When we leave this planet, even if we were able to leave the solar system, what might we expect to find? Planets? Even planets that are inhabited?

Life is a community of three types of existence – **plants, animals, and humans**. The plants manufacture the three nutrients on which all animals and plants live:

sugar

starch

protein

All other vegetable ingredients are chemically produced by the plants from these three basic constituents. In the production of the three nutrients themselves, the plants divide water into hydrogen and oxygen. Animals and humans then burn up the hydrogen and oxygen compounds of carbon to produce water again. This cycle is maintained by three porphyritic compounds: **chlorophyll, haemine, and cobalamine**.

If any extraterrestrial life exists at some vast distance from us, it has to be similar to that existing on our planet because the three elements capable of forming double bonds are unique in the universe. Only they provide a chemical framework through which electrons or protons can wander. Even if we travel hundreds of billions of kilometres, we would not be even one step further on the way to finding out about the purpose of life. But there must be something that could justify such a journey. What might that be?

At this point in my life humankind was preparing to travel to the Moon. It had been some time since J F Kennedy had made his famous speech about the space between the Earth and the Moon as an ocean which would have to be crossed, and as posing a challenge to the whole of humanity. I was fascinated by the dearth of information on the powerful engines in the Moon rockets. The Americans were dominant in the design of liquid-oxygen and liquid-hydrogen combustion, particularly in view of their recently developed computers, with the help of which the solution of such problems as the necessary cooling of combustion chambers was child's play.

Of the enormous rocket, nothing would return to Earth except for a tiny module in which the three men were jammed like sardines, probably praying that the parachutes would open. The whole programme would cost one hundred million dollars. Instead of finding Indians and gold, the astronauts would only return with a sack full of stones. But these stones would then be subjected to chemical analysis, and we would then at last know whether rocks on the Moon were identical to those on the Earth and whether their age was also the same.

For we still do not know whether the Moon really broke away from the Earth, as assumed in the fission theory propounded by the astronomer George H Darwin.[1] I came to the conclusion that the fission theory must be correct. The alternative theory – the capture of a passing asteroid – leads to physically impossible contradictions. But if the Moon is actually part of the Earth, the Earth-Moon system must consist of two planets – it is effectively a double planet. When the Moon is in front of the Earth in relation to the sun, it is the third planet in the solar system. When it is behind the Earth, the Earth is the third planet. I found it incredibly exciting that this double planet is linked to the number 3. Equally exciting was my notion that perhaps the existence of life on our planet is necessarily linked to the existence of our Moon. Without the Moon, all the water on the Earth would not move. The oceans would only be immense static pools.

The time the Moon requires for its orbit of the Earth[2] is one sidereal month or

$$27.32 \text{ days}$$

At the end of this period the Moon assumes the same position in relation to the stars.

Every student of medicine must learn the following sentence off by heart: the period of growth in the human womb between conception and birth has a statistic duration of ten sidereal months, or 273 days. It is a proven fact that the female oestral cycle follows the true astronomical rhythm and not the cycle of full Moon to full Moon which is two days longer. For astronomers, who are generally all male, this fact is entirely irrelevant. But what an extraordinary coincidence there is between the figure of 273 days and absolute zero, the temperature of −273°C!

There it is again – the correspondence between the Moon and water. To me, water is the most mysterious substance in our solar system. Although water has a key role in biology – being the medium of life, for all cellular reactions take place in a watery medium – the decisive point is nevertheless still not appreciated.

For some profoundly mysterious reason, approximately every 55 millionth water molecule is split. The trivial fundamental equation of chemistry

$$H_2O \Leftrightarrow H^+ + OH^-$$

means that water is always an inseparable mixture of three components:

$$H_3O^+ \; H_2O \; H_1O^-$$

Anybody bold enough to attempt to separate these constituents would surely fail. And we want to travel to space although we do not even have an explanation for the three-fold nature of water! It became less and less clear to me what we could really do there – despite my passionate interest in rocket technology.

Now, after my dream, I was convinced that space travel would only begin when we had solved the cosmic riddle.

My studies were coming to a close. My last assignment at the university was a very fateful one, as I would later see in retrospect.

I had to produce a chemical compound first isolated by a young German chemist called Ernst Otto Fischer: the now famous dibenzene-chromium. This compound consists of two benzene rings, lying on top of each other like the two slices of a sandwich. Between them, there is a zerovalent chromium atom floating. But nobody really knows how a zerovalent atom can form a chemical compound. I quickly discovered that a whole series of my predecessors had attempted to isolate this compound without managing it. There was therefore little chance of my being successful. Once, to my great annoyance, a long mercury thermometer fell into the flask containing the dark broth and smashed. How could this happen to me, who had always been so proud of my deft chemist's hands? But then I had a sudden idea – mercury!

In the sixteenth century, mercury was one of the three materials – **mercury, sulphur** and **salt** – that the famous chemist and doctor Paracelsus believed to be the basis of all other materials. This was a new departure from the understanding that had prevailed since ancient times – that there is a fundamental duality involving the elements sulphur and mercury. Only by including a third element could the true essence of nature, its trinity, be understood.[3]

I did not ponder this for long. I dashed to the chemical dispensary, obtained a glass of mercury and shook it on top of the mercury from the thermometer. Perhaps my predecessors had not managed to create a reaction with the aluminium swimming in the soup. I anxiously waited for the moment that would show my experiment had succeeded, when I would be able to see beautiful dark-red crystals forming on a cooling rod in the high vacuum. At least, that was how the author of the synthesis process had described it. And then I really did see them form! Professor Linke was enthusiastic about the result and asked me many times how I had managed it. I did not tell him and forgot about the episode for some time afterwards.

The oral examinations for my degree began with the subject of organic chemistry. My examiner, Professor Birkhofer, remarked after half an hour that I was one of those people who knew everything. He would therefore ask me about something I did not know. A few years previously a chemist had created a compound which looked like a sandwich with a zerovalent chromium atom between the two layers. Could I imagine how such a bond could be produced? I was indeed well able to imagine it. I described how I would take a trivalent chromium salt and, as a first step, reduce it with a metal dust, for example aluminium powder, to form monovalent chromium. I could even imagine adding a dash of mercury to the reaction mixture. I then discussed the further steps until a zerovalent chromium had been reached.

Professor Birkhofer leapt up, embraced me and explained that he had never had such a clever candidate in the chemistry examinations. He then gave me the desired grade.

It was only when I again found myself in the corridor that I realized what I had actually experienced. This was the second time that I had encountered this zerovalent chromium atom. It could not be a coincidence any more. But I still had no idea at that time that I would one day come face to face with the discoverer of this compound. Professor Birkhofer had said that Ernst Otto Fischer would one day receive the Nobel Prize for this compound and I had expressed my agreement. He had been awarded the Nobel Prize a long time before we finally met, many years later.

I went looking for Professor Fehér, the director of the Institute for Organic Chemistry.

'Well, you probably now want to become an organic chemist,' he said when we met.

'No, Professor. I did not study chemistry so that I could explore the compounds of one single element for the rest of my life. I would like to become an inorganic chemist because all chemistry and all elements interest me.'

I saw the old man's eyes light up.

'Such words, Mr Plichta, are scarcely heard any more. I have a position for you in a department where a lot of experimental imagination is required. But the work at this centre is not entirely without risks. Courage is what is needed. Have you got courage?'

Instead of giving him an answer, I asked expectantly: 'Which department?' I felt as if I had been in a deep sleep.

'We are the only institute in the world that produces silicon hydride in large quantities.'

I had come across the existence of the benzines of silicon in my chemistry book as a boy. As time passed I became increasingly sure that this substance would have a major influence on my life. Shortly before my final school exams I had made a fiery speech to my fellow pupils, declaring that I intended to be the first to manufacture compounds from the silanes. During my later studies at university, however, I had had nothing more to do with them.

I was now almost speechless in anticipation. The professor was just about to explain about the materials involved when I found my voice.

'How far have you got now with the silanes?'

'Well,' he replied, 'we have only got as far as Stock[4] did, up to the tetrasilanes.'

'And have you managed to make any compounds?'

'No. The silanes always explode with all reagents. We have only managed to synthesize a compound with iodine.'

'I was experimenting with explosive substances even as a young boy. I would really like to work in your department. I want to make compounds with silane. It must be possible. Chemistry has shown that everything is possible provided it is approached in the correct way. Working with silanes has been a dream of mine for so long. I never knew that you possessed them.'

The eyes of the old wolf shone like beacons.

Silanes are liquids similar to the petroleum hydrocarbons we fill our petrol tanks with. One difference is that they are self-igniting and, once they have started to burn, they blaze like hellfire and are impossible to extinguish. If the great Alfred Stock had managed to synthesize compounds of them he might even have received the Nobel Prize, but as it happened no use could be found for the silanes, and after his death nobody in the world wanted to produce such a hellish concoction.

Mr Fehér had been able to persuade the German research community to make considerable funds available for research in less dangerous, more elegant and easily manageable forms of presentation. He now had a quantity of the four isolated silanes, based on one, two, three and four silicon atoms. He was as clever as Professor Stock had been.

Because the compounds could not be manufactured, he wanted at least to produce higher silanes – namely those based on five, six, seven or eight silicon atoms. He now had plans to manufacture large quantities of raw silane in a new semi-

59

industrial laboratory so that they would be able at last to isolate minute quantities of the much sought after higher silanes.

But everything turned out quite differently.

NOTES

1 The distribution of landmasses on this planet is irregular. Almost half of the surface of the Earth, the Pacific Ocean, is one vast area of water. All five continents have been proved once to have been one gigantic proto-continent (Pangea). According to A E Ringwood, the Moon must have separated from the Earth at the time of the separation of the iron core and the silicate outer stratum in the Earth. The sinking of the heavy iron to the centre of the Earth would have caused the rotation of the planet to increase, just as a pirouetting dancer increases her speed when she draws her arms together. Because of this, part of the Earth's shell could have flown off, resulting also in a loss of the Earth's momentum of spin. This spin momentum must therefore be contained at present in the lunar orbit (A Unsöld).

2 We humans on the other hand use the synodic month of 29.53 days in our calendars. This is the time the Moon needs to attain the same position in relation to the sun in one circuit. This period is longer than the sidereal month because the Earth has in the meantime moved on in its own course around the sun.

3 Paracelsus was one of the few who were centuries ahead of their time.

4 Alfred Stock developed an apparatus for working with substances that are sensitive to air by the total exclusion of oxygen or in a vacuum. He was the first to manage the pure synthesis of mono-, di-, tri-, and tetrasilanes through the reaction of magnesium silicate with inorganic acids. He was one of the great inorganic chemists of the 20th century.

CHAPTER SIX

VISION AND DETERMINATION

After I had submitted the thesis for my master's degree, I began work on my PhD, together with another graduate chemist, Rolf Guillery. Two laboratories and the excellent high-vacuum apparatus of my predecessor were available to us. I proceeded under the assumption that the dangerous silanes could be better managed with two pairs of skilled chemists' hands.

Monophenyl disilane was to be our first silane compound. I wanted to use two different ways to produce it, to exclude any chance of failure. The synthesis was soon achieved. We showed Mr Fehér the identical nuclear resonance spectra of the new compounds. The professor acted at once: I was immediately included among the Institute's salaried staff. I had been anticipating a so-called 'quarter' position, and that Rolf would be given the same status because we had, after all, succeeded in synthesizing the compound as a team. Instead, I was given a full position with the second highest salary rate for state employees in Germany, and with the strict instruction from the Director of the Institute not to share as much as one mark with my colleagues. The position was paid for by the German Research Society. I was told that the director had had the money frozen for years, and had been holding it ready for the chemist that achieved the breakthrough in silane chemistry.

Thus began the rise and fall of Peter Plichta at the Institute for Inorganic Chemistry at the University of Cologne.

The hours spent in my laboratory in the Institute were to be the happiest time of my life. One morning I woke up, filled with a wonderful feeling, and went as if guided by providence straight to the library of the Chemistry Institute. I was drawn as if by a magnet to a certain shelf and took down a yearbook with publications in chemistry. I opened the book and found an article on the substitution of phenyl groups with silicon atoms which had a free hydrogen atom. The residual phenyl could easily be replaced in condensed halogen hydrides by halogen residuals. I immediately realized how my own work had to proceed. It had to be possible to produce tetraphenyl-disilane and from this compound to replace two benzine residuals by two bromine atoms. All further steps were then clear.

I have deliberately used specialist chemistry jargon in describing this process so that the reader will get an impression of the language of chemists. It is not necessary to understand all the details.

My approach would result in an interim product – the symmetrical diphenyl-dibromine-disilane with two asymmetrical silicon atoms.[1]

$$\begin{array}{ccc} | & & | \\ \mathrm{H} - \mathrm{Si*} & - & \mathrm{Si*} - \mathrm{H} \\ | & & | \end{array}$$

With its two free hydrogen atoms it is in exact stereochemical correspondence to tartaric acid, with which Pasteur made one of the most important discoveries in chemistry over one hundred years ago.

So this was the reason I had been on a cloud from the time I left my bedside until I reached the library: asymmetrical twin atoms! In chemistry an asymmetrical silicon atom means a silicon atom – represented by the symbol Si – holding four different atoms or atom groups on its four free arms. A chemical silane compound with such an asymmetrical silicon atom – marked here by * – always occurs in two different symmetries that are not mutually congruent. Now, when two such silicon atoms are joined in a bond, as in the above formula, a total of four symmetries must exist for this compound. This can be demonstrated by a clear example from everyday life.

Let us say we want to lay a square table with knives and forks for four people. The front place at the table (1) will have the fork on the left and the knife on the right and these will be inverted and laterally transposed across the table at the opposite place (3). This will also be the case for places (2) and (4). Most chemists are not aware of this example, and this prevents the two opposite asymmetrical atoms from being recognized as inverted in relation to each other. Because I have a twin brother who can reasonably be described as my opposite, I considered the synthesis of the first asymmetrical silane compound with two points of inversion as not only interesting from a chemical point of view but also as a predetermined introduction to research into the theory of space and topology. There it was again – the nagging question of my youth concerning the unknown structure of absolute space.

I showed Rolf the eight steps by which one could start with phenylchlorosilane – a purely industrial product – and achieve a pure disilane. We procured two ten-litre canisters of the substance and began synthesizing. We continued day and night, and at weekends and on holidays. Parallel to this process we also intended to attack silanes directly with reacting agents.

Four silanes were known at that time. Mono- and disilane are gaseous substances. We had a supply of them filled in small steel cylinders. Trisilane and tetrasilane are liquids. They were stored in airtight containers at the Institute. Alfred Stock had attempted to convert silanes from halogens, and the process had caused mighty explosions. I had an idea: we would have to dilute bromine with dichlorodifluoromethane, cool the solution, and carefully let it drop onto a strongly diluted trisilane solution that was cooled to −80°C. For this experiment I would, however, require a very special dropping funnel which, to provide a surrounding vacuum, would require three glass walls which scarcely seemed possible at the time. But because it had to work, it did work.

We prepared to brominate the disilane and solved all technical problems. We practised the individual steps of the experiment. We were finally ready on Easter Sunday morning, 1968. I had asked Helga, who had in the meantime become my wife, to come with us to Cologne and take photographs of the two chemists with their bullet-proof face shields and all their apparatus. After she had taken the photographs she drove back to Düsseldorf. She was not aware that we really were putting our lives at risk.

When small drops of the bromine solution were released, the brown colour of the chemical disappeared. When I began to let the drops fall more quickly, we were surprised to witness a new phenomenon. Electrical flashes appeared over the cold liquid and ceased a few centimetres above the stirred solution. We then realized why the silanes manufactured earlier had exploded with a bang in the ears of all our predecessors.

After a moment of awed wonder, I asked Rolf: 'Have you ever heard of such a thing – an electric storm over a liquid 100 degrees below zero?'

He shook his head.

'The day my brother got married I saw lightning in the distance with an enormous number of flashes coming through a floating bank of clouds.'

I suddenly had a brainwave: 'We are never going to see this again, because the next time we will work with an even more dilute solution. But if we used chlorine instead of bromine we would be blown up together with the whole laboratory.'

'Yes,' Rolf replied. 'We would then be blown up all right!'

'But do you still want to go on?' I asked him carefully.

'Of course I want to go on,' he replied.

We then managed to readjust a gas chromatography apparatus so that we could use it to separate explosive and aggressive substances. Soon, various different disilane bromides had been separated and were standing on the desk.

The way was now free to carry out any number of substitution reactions, of the type done with silane chains in organic chemistry. We then wanted to chlorinate trisilane, an experiment which really did turn out to be explosive.

The plan to manufacture the first disilane compounds with asymmetrical twin atoms had also finally been realized after months of effort. It had worked. The substance had contained, as tartaric acids do, two free hydrogen atoms that have entirely the same chemistry. We had therefore hoped to find a single free line, a singlet, for the two protons.

I had gone with Rolf to the organic chemists, filled with tense anticipation. We inorganic chemists did not possess our own nuclear spectrograph. The three of us stood in the measuring room and watched the plotter running across the paper. I clenched my fist as we waited for the moment when it would surge upward. Then suddenly it rose like a rocket, held a moment, trembled and fell again. We repeated the measurement several times. Each time the plotter trembled again. We showed the records to the organic chemist, Professor Roth, who very quickly had an explanation: 'There's some dirt in the substance.'

After we had gone back to the lab, I thought about it and decided to replace the two free bromine atoms with two further hydrogen atoms. The symmetrical diphenyl-disilane that would be created would possess four similar protons but would have no more asymmetrical silicon atoms. I was eager to see what would happen with this 'impurity'. When we made a spectroscope analysis of this compound, we found a beautiful singlet; there was no sign of any trembling this time.

'It really was probably caused by impurities,' said Professor Fehér.

I took a pen and sketched the formula for the disilane with the two asymmetrical silicon atoms. Below this I wrote the same formula, only this time with two asymmetrical germanium atoms. Rolf recognized immediately what I was getting at.

$$\text{H} - \overset{|}{\underset{|}{\text{Ge}^*}} - \overset{|}{\underset{|}{\text{Ge}^*}} - \text{H}$$

'How do you intend to do that?'

I replied, 'With germanium. We chlorinate it, hang on phenyl groups, and try to link up two germanium atoms.'

I ordered a whole kilogram of germanium powder from the chemistry store. It cost over DM2,000. I then waited for Professor Fehér to come dashing into the laboratory. He turned up, sure enough, and in a very excited state.

'How can you order DM2,000 worth of germanium?'

I replied with very deliberate politeness: 'I would like to manufacture a digermanium compound and prove that the oscillation in the plotter is not caused by an impurity, but by two twin compounds. But if two thousand marks is too much for you, then I shall pay for it myself.'

At that moment the Professor showed that he had a real

understanding of chemistry.

'Mr Plichta, has anyone in the world ever made digermanium compounds? Compounds with free hydrogen atoms?'

I replied that it had not actually been done yet.

'And how do you intend to do it?'

I held up my left and right hands, like two symmetrical atoms: 'With my hands.'

He stared at me, nodded, and left the laboratory.

But not without turning around once and saying: 'In the future you can buy as much germanium as you need in this Institute.'

'But I also need a nuclear spectrograph operator,' I called after him.

'You'll get one.'

I was also assigned several undergraduates and an apprentice.

Because of the danger, Rolf and I carried out the chlorination of the trisilane at night, and only when we were alone. I had told Paul that something would happen one night.

All the preparations had taken much longer than planned.

At the moment when the chlorine solution was running into the hollow funnel – from which it was to drop further into the very weak silane solution – the telephone suddenly rang. I temporarily halted the experiment by carefully turning back the high-vacuum tap just before the first drops fell into the solution. I walked to the desk and pulled the glove from my left hand. With my wet hand I lifted the receiver and took off my helmet.

Behind me, a hairdryer began to sound. I turned around. Rolf had taken off the glove from his right hand and was just about to turn the high-vacuum tap with his unprotected right hand, while holding the hairdryer with his left hand.

'Stop!' I shouted. I threw down the receiver, pulled down my helmet, grabbed the heavy iron lamp with my bare left hand, ran to Rolf and tried to check the position of the tap with the light cone. Without a strong light Rolf was not able to see anything through the bulletproof protective glass on the laboratory table. There was a flash of lightning, as bright and forceful as in a storm, and immediately afterwards came the roar of thunder. I was seized by the blast and flew across the room, filled with a euphoric feeling of happiness.

Rolf and I were taken to the university clinic. The bulletproof clothing I had ordered had saved our lives.

As soon as I was back on my feet again, I arranged for a new funnel to be built. It was fitted with a high-vacuum reducer valve, and I extended the control knob with a flow regulator tube several metres long. There was some excitement in the Institute because some people were anticipating that I would not be so lucky in my second attempt to chlorinate trisilane. One day soon afterwards I visited Rolf in hospital. I sat by his bed and told him my news: 'Rolf, last night I chlorinated the trisilane. It worked!'

Rolf and I finished a voluntary secondary course of study at the nuclear chemical institution – a radiochemical laboratory course and thereafter the advanced laboratory course in nuclear chemistry. At the same time we attended the lectures of Professor Herr, the director of the Institute of Nuclear Chemistry. Because we both had already completed a four-semester practical course in experimental physics, we were becoming increasingly interested in nuclear chemical and nuclear physical associations. My involvement in these two subjects led me back to the critical question that had occupied my mind even as a child – the question of the structure of the atom.

Because all atoms are composed of only three types of elementary particles, the laws governing the atomic nucleus and atomic 'shells' are very easy to comprehend. These laws were, however, very difficult to discover because the various dependencies can only be integrated within a satisfactory theory by a series of extremely imaginative experiments. I was soon to be 30 years old and was still occupied with three central questions:

- Why do the atomic numbers of the elements – the number of protons in the stable elements – run straight through the numbers from 1, 2, 3, ... to 83, and why should the elements 43 and 61 be missing?
- Why does each element not exist as an 'only child'? For instance, whereas phosphorus occurs only once, possessing sixteen neutrons as well as fifteen protons, chlorine occurs twice, once with seventeen protons and eighteen neutrons

and once with seventeen protons and twenty neutrons.
• Why do the orbiting electrons have precisely four features, which physicists call the four quantum numbers?

Whereas the positively charged protons are concentrated in an unimaginably small nucleus, the particle with the opposite charge cannot form any such conglomeration because they are mutually repellent. This statement is, however, not without qualification. The electrons closest to the atomic nucleus behave in an apparently arbitrary way. They are found like pairs of sparrows sitting on a wire. Some secret law tells them that in the innermost orbit one pair may sit, the next orbit can take a total of four pairs, the third orbit has nine, and there are sixteen in the fourth orbit. The mathematical law for this had a quadratic nature since these numbers – 1, 4, 9, 16 – can be described as the squares of the numbers 1, 2, 3 and 4.

Because further shells then follow, it might be supposed that 25 pairs are located in the fifth orbit. In fact, the law only applies to the first four shells. Furthermore, we know that there are only four types of electrons in the shells.

All of this constituted a very serious problem for me. I had previously assumed that everything has a three-fold nature, just as all atoms in the universe are composed of protons, neutrons and electrons. If this law holds good, how can it be that the orbiting electrons possess four quantum numbers?[2]

In the course of my investigation into the quadruple feature in quantum numbers I began to notice four-fold phenomena in all types of fields. We see in the sky the four phases of the Moon and on the Earth the four seasons. DNA works with four bases; the advanced primates have four physical extremities; and the electron levels in the inert gases are filled with four pairs of electrons. I had always found it almost mystical how elegantly the surface area of a globe can be calculated by multiplying the surface of the outline circle by the integer 4. All life on this planet is powered by the light of the sun, and where does this light come from? It arises simply by virtue of the fact that four protons are transformed in the helium isotope of mass 4. It would conversely be of no use whatever to humankind if, instead, the process in the sun involved an atom with a mass number 5 produced by five protons. How can some phenomena

68

be strictly triple whereas others are quadruple?

Of these three questions, the third one seemed to me to be the one most easily solved. The squares of the numbers 1, 2, 3 and 4 – also called the main quantum numbers of the electron cloud – must have something to do with the numbers themselves.

This is the way it was seen too by Arnold Sommerfeld, who spent many years of his life subjecting problems of theoretical physics to investigations in number theory. Eight of his pupils received the Nobel Prize; only the true master himself was not given the award. He was fully understood only by Albert Einstein and Max Planck, and by Werner Heisenberg towards the end of his life. These three knew that if there was a divine plan, it could be based on nothing else but numbers. This notion is in the classic platonic tradition. Sommerfeld's successors did not pursue the idea because they considered numbers to be mystical: they were proud to have excluded any kind of plan – and thus God – from their concept of the world.

Sommerfeld knew that two elements attempting to form a bond would try to share their electrons in such a way that they would have eight electrons at their highest energy levels, four electron twins. These four electron pairs are not all the same. Three pairs, referred to as p-electrons, make up one family, whereas the fourth pair is not related to them. Even today, scientists have not the faintest idea why this is so. They accept it as it is and are proud of what they know.

I sat in Professor Herr's study and heard that there is an artificial fourth radioactive decay conductor. On a piece of paper I jotted down

$$3 + 1$$

Below this I sketched a circle and drew in it in the form of a cross: the four spaces so formed within the circle I could now think of as four pairs of electron twins.

In one of the upper pairs I wrote the letter 's', and I wrote the letter 'p' in the three other pairs. The drawing reminded me of the table laid with knives and forks for four. If one of these were made of gold and three of silver, this would have no effect on the spatial geometry. The silver pairs seemed to me like reflections of the gold cutlery in place one.

That was the only advantage I had gained over Sommerfeld –

the realization that nature has in two cases expanded a three-fold phenomenon to a four-fold one: the radioactive decay series and the electrons in the inert gases.

I then immediately thought of a third example: We see three colours with our eyes, using three different chromatic cells. Two of these colours can be combined to form a new, fourth colour. With these four colours – red, yellow, green and blue – we can then see the entire spectrum of all colours, well over a hundred.

Professor Herr consistently gave me encouragement. In one of his lectures he was discussing the pure isotope of arsenic, element 33, when I stood up and interrupted him.

'Professor Herr, is there any explanation as to why the element is a pure isotope and not a multiple isotope?'

He hesitated a moment before answering: 'Mr Plichta, we have no explanation for it. We haven't the slightest idea.'

The opportunity had now arrived for me to ask the question I had wanted to ask at university on at least one occasion.

'Could it be that everything we know, and of which we are so proud to know, is completely meaningless as long as we cannot answer the question why pure and multiple isotopes exist at all?'

'I would like to answer this question honestly,' replied Professor Herr. 'Something entirely unimagined could in fact be responsible for it and make sense of it all.'

Professor Fehér summoned me once more around this time. He greeted me like a father and pleaded with me to stop studying law, as I had been doing in my spare time. He told me that it was a total waste of time because I would probably become a professor of chemistry very quickly after my exams.

I reminded him: 'Professor, remember that Leibniz was a lawyer.'

I was suddenly struck with the realization that all of jurisprudence is generally divided into three main areas – **civil law**, **criminal law**, and **administrative law** – just as chemistry contains three types of elements. I was surprised. In physics, for example, magnetism has always had a triple aspect corresponding to paramagnetism, and diamagnetism, and ferromagnetism, we can assume this to be due to a general principle of nature that we have not yet discovered. But what can possibly be behind the triple structure of jurisprudence? Should I ask the lawyers? That would probably do no good since they too accept everything simply as it is. Could it be that all my studies of law served only to show me that the triplicate is no exclusive feature of natural sciences, but is also something deeper and eternal?

I had formerly dreamt of becoming a professor one day. Now I was no longer sure whether I really wanted to devote my life to research. The best thing for me might well be to withdraw completely with my PhD under my arm and spend ten years meditating on these problems. If someone would support me financially for the next ten years, I would be in a position to start deciphering nature's plan at the age of 40. I would then also be more mature, more experienced, and in the middle of my life.

Actually, I had no other option but to continue studying. Could this be reconciled with a professorship? What I wanted to find out could certainly not be gleaned from any specialist knowledge. To do what I wanted I would have to know everything my precursors had thought and discovered. It would therefore be necessary to become familiar with the history of the sciences, including the history of philosophy and mathematics. Superficial knowledge would not be enough. I would, of course, also have to undertake a study of biology, the third natural science after physics and chemistry.

What else would I have to learn? Medicine and astronomy – and, of course, philosophy. Without acknowledging the major thinkers of the West as well as Indian and Chinese philosophy I would have no hope of making progress.

Indeed, I really ought to study theoretical physics – but I was warned by an inner voice that that would be a cul-de-sac. The empirical findings of quantum mechanics are correct, but the theoretical suppositions inferred from them have tended only to obscure many aspects of our understanding of nature. The extension of theories of quantum mechanics is even proclaimed as an approach supported by nature. The essence of physics can, however, never have any real contact with quantum mechanics. We do not know why electrons are located so precisely at energy levels governed by apparently sound numerical laws. But it is possible, for instance, to continue accumulating

71

empirical data by spectral analysis to a degree that allows us forget the shortcomings in our basic understanding of the world.

Preparing for the oral exams for my PhD went on for six months. The date for the examination was continually being postponed. I was in no way prepared for the trauma that I then experienced.

The day had passed like all others at this time. I was sitting in bed at night. Some textbooks lay on my night-table and my wife Helga was asleep beside me. I had a physics textbook opened on my knees. For a moment my eyes had run over the Hahn-Einstein equation

$$h\nu = mc^2$$

While meditating on this, my thoughts began to wander and I was filled with the mystery of the formula in which the essence of both nuclear physics and atomic physics is concentrated. What could possibly be behind this equation? How often in my life had I dwelt on this formula?[3]

Suddenly I saw an apparition. We do not know what a vision really is, and we certainly do not know why visions occur at certain moments.

My eyes were distracted from the book. I looked up through an infinite black space. Nothing in the room had changed, except that now I was overcome by a feeling of infinite happiness. As the thought 'What's going on?' flew through my mind I heard a voice as if it was speaking to someone else:

'That is the man who has found out everything.'

I was overwhelmed by the notion: 'Everything? But that's impossible.' But then I began to realize what the vision really meant. There was more than just a formula behind the Planck-Einstein equation. If that was true then it was also certain that I would be the person who found the solution to the riddle. All I needed was the certainty that something of decisive significance was hidden in the equation. The rest I could manage with intelligence and commitment. I was about to wake Helga with a cry of joy. But then something else happened. From that infinite dark space something else approached me and began to take shape, it was a young woman who had died, died young. She was wearing a white dress and appeared to be sleeping. It was my wife Helga. As I was overwhelmed with horror, the same voice spoke from outside:

'Helga's death is only the reverse of his finding out everything.'

I began to scream and the space disappeared.

Helga awoke and looked at me in puzzlement as I burst into tears.

'What's the matter? '

'I have just seen an apparition. I shall solve the riddle of the universe, and because of it you will die young.'

Helga too was shocked at first, but then composed herself and tried to comfort me.

'But Peter, we all have to die sometime. It is not so important when.'

But I was deeply troubled at the notion that the discovery of a scientific secret should somehow be linked to the death of my wife. It was as if it had all been determined and I was simply playing out my part, no more than a puppet. We looked at each other in mutually helpless dismay. What could Helga be thinking? She knew that I loved science and how committed I was to discovering truth.

Helga brought me something to drink and a small jar of sleeping tablets. Knowledgeable about pharmaceuticals, I remember I was irritated by the fact that the medicine was available without prescription (as would be unthinkable today).

I became sleepy at last, but I could not get the word *pharmacy* out of my head. It was as if it held a special significance for my future.

We never spoke about this vision again.

NOTES

1 The bromine and phenyl residues are not included in the molecular formula because a reader with no formal knowledge of chemistry would recognize only the two symmetrical silicon atoms. This same procedure is later repeated with germanium or carbon atoms. The letter H of course stands for a hydrogen atom.

2 The scientist that coined the term 'quantum number' also listed the following alternative characteristics of the electrons: 1) their membership of a particular orbital shell; 2) their specific features (s, p, d or f) on a shell; 3) their magnetic behaviour; and 4) their clockwise or anti-clockwise rotation. This description is, however, entirely empirical, even though it does reveal a praiseworthy attempt at classification and explanation.

3 Read h multiplied by v (Greek *nu*) equals mass (m) multiplied by the speed

of light (c) squared. This equation contains two natural constants: Planck's quantum of energy h and the speed of light c; v is the frequency of an electromagnetic wave (the frequency is the number of oscillations in the wave each second). The equation actually combines two equations: $E = hv$ (Planck) and $E = mc^2$ (Einstein). It is the central formula of quantum mechanics and is not compatible with classical physics. The term *quantum* comes from Latin and means 'How much?' Planck discovered that not only is matter present in particles, but so also is energy. The term 'quantum mechanics' was coined in order to reconcile the laws prevailing in atomic physics with those of classical physics. Nobody in physics knows why the speed of light is connected with the quantum of motion. Because both natural constants occur in this equation, the question is considered closed.

CHAPTER SEVEN

THE FINAL QUESTION

Physical chemistry was a mandatory subject in all chemistry exams. However, Rolf and I wanted to have our knowledge of physics and nuclear chemistry documented, and we therefore applied to the faculty to be examined in these two subjects for a PhD. We were successful. This was partly due to the fact that I had become quite notorious after the 'explosion' of my laboratory, and partly because the holder of the chair in nuclear chemistry was able to exercise considerable influence. He had been an assistant to the Nobel Prize winner Otto Hahn and was later instrumental in the creation of the nuclear research centre in Jülich for the state of North Rhine-Westphalia. He therefore had a lot of influence in the city of Cologne.

The examination in nuclear chemistry went on for a long time and was difficult. There was a bronze bust of Otto Hahn in the examination room and I had the strange sensation that he, too, was taking part in the test. I impressed Professor Herr with details from a paper of Hahn which cannot be found in the books, and it was therefore with something of a flourish that I finally took leave of my examiners.

Professor Herr must have written something unusual on the examination papers. In any case, that evening, when the physics examination began, Professor Hauser looked at me in disbelief and said that Professor Herr had never awarded such a grade before. We sat in a small room of the dean's office in the main university building. Professor Hauser appeared to be contemplating something for a moment, but then he spoke.

'It seems I don't need to even start examining you in physics. I shall give you the highest grade and dispense with the examination. I have already met your fellow student (he meant Rolf) and he also knew everything. I was curious to find out which of you was the leading light in your partnership. I now know why everybody is talking about you at the faculty. However, the two of us can't just walk out of the door now. We shall have to pass the next 20 minutes somehow.'

He looked at me for some time and asked: 'Have you ever wondered why silicon atoms are not able to form double bonds? Silicon belongs to the fourth group, directly under carbon, and according to the rules of physics and chemistry it should be able to form double bonds.'

I replied hesitantly with quantum mechanic formulations.

He must have noticed my hesitation.

'Perhaps you don't really believe what you have just said? Please remember that this is no longer an examination. I have already given you the highest grade.'

The time had come for me to make a decision, now, during my final examination. Should I be courageous and state the extent of my doubts on the prevailing theory of physics?

'Professor, I consider such terms as "d-orbitals" and "hybridization" to be just another way of concealing how little we know.'

He stared at me and addressed me for the first time using the title 'Doctor': 'Doctor Plichta, are you implying in what you have just said that you consider the entire theory of electrons – the foundation of chemistry and physics – not only mildly abberrant but completely wrong?'

I then replied to this astonishingly clearly formulated question, the final question formally put to me in the University of Cologne: 'Professor Hauser, I consider the central notion in the electron theory to be completely wrong. Something totally different must be hidden in this phenomenon.'

He then said, with the same note of finality, 'I think so too.'

We sat and looked across at each other. He continued the conversation.

'Doctor Plichta, you know you are actually both chemist and

physicist? I would like to know if you consider yourself more a chemist or a physicist?'

I replied: 'I am wholeheartedly a chemist. But there are problems in physics which I can not put out of my mind.'

He accepted my reply and went on: 'Do you know what I think? I believe that there is a man sitting in front of me who in ten years' time will have found a solution to the outstanding problems of modern chemistry and physics. In ten years you will be something different from what you are today. You will be a theoretical physicist!'

Immediately the words from my vision shot through my head: 'This is the man who will find out everything.' I would have to be careful I did not betray my thoughts: I tried to look casual.

'It is true that I intend to seek qualifications and become a professor. But then I would like to spend some time in the chemical industry, in the place where money is made and not spent. I shall have to leave this ivory tower. Max Planck and Albert Einstein also tried to find a solution to this puzzle and failed. If I become involved here and am finally successful, the envy of my fellow teachers and researchers would be the death of me.'

I was suddenly certain that his final sentence would have a decisive influence on my life.

'Doctor Plichta, I'm now sure of one thing – you will be successful. In ten years. Wherever you are then, call me!'

I too was now sure.

By the time I started my qualifying period in Cologne, Rolf and I were no longer working together. I was given a position as an assistant on a government salary, whereas Rolf did not receive any offer of a job from the Institute. It annoyed me that my boss could do something so stupid. I was also very surprised. I remonstrated with Herr Fehér and told him straight that I considered it totally wrong that a pair of chemists such as Rolf and I, who had shown they could work so well as a team, were now to be separated.

I had also hoped that I would fairly quickly be given the use of higher silanes – the pentasilanes and hexasilanes – from our semi-industrial plant. I would then immediately begin the cycling process. Herr Fehér would thus become, at the age of 70, quite a famous man, and so would I. But the wheels of administration in this Institute did not turn as quickly as I had anticipated, with the result that no higher silanes were forthcoming for the time being.

I had driven past the towers of Erdöl Chemie, a subsidiary of the great chemical corporation Bayer, hundreds of times on the autobahn between Düsseldorf and Cologne. In this factory, chain carbon compounds were subject to pyrolysis.[1] But on this particular occasion as I was again driving past I suddenly realized what I had failed to see all along – the possibility of exposing the three existing chain silanes to heat. What would happen at a medium temperature of, say, 300°C? In the chemistry textbooks of the time it was stated that higher silanes could not exist because they are unstable at room temperature. Now chemistry books are written just the same as all other books. In this way, not only do the works of humankind increase and multiply, but also their errors.

I carried out an experiment together with a colleague. We used a glass tube filled with glass wool and a little platinized asbestos through which trisilane was passed in a vacuum at 360°C. The process was repeated many times and the resulting fluid oil was separated by a gas-chromatographic preparative process, for such residues can no longer be separated by distillation. As I had expected, chain and branched higher silanes were created – penta-, hexa-, hepta-, octa- and nonasilanes – which until then had been totally unknown. The pyrolysis of tetrasilane was even more successful.

So there they were at last – the higher silanes, the diesel-oil-equivalents of silicon. Scientists had been looking for them for 50 years.

It would now be easy to manufacture these oils in industrial processes from the three basic materials **magnesium**, **silicon**, and **sulphuric acid**, which cost little to produce. There are already enough higher hydrocarbons around, such as occur in crude oil. These were created in an entirely natural process by sunlight and pressure over many millions of years. But nobody had guessed that it would be possible to create such compounds from silicon instead of from carbon. I now held them in my hands and knew that I had made one of the last great discoveries in organic chemistry. The applications that could be found for them – how they might be used – were things I did not know, however. And this is the essential point of the discovery of a new chemical substance: it must be of some use to people.

I knew I had made a serious error. For 15 years my superior had been hoping that one day he would be able to hold these test tubes in his hands. He had improved Stock's method by the use of modern apparatus. But now I had got in there before him, and it had only taken me one weekend. I would have to be very careful, for the political intrigues in a chemistry institute are no different from those in a Chinese imperial court. Not only the emperor suffers loss of face but also all the eunuchs, and their desire for revenge is dangerous.

Could Professor Fehér consider my success to be also his? He had made the claim and his pupil had proved it – not only can compounds be created from silanes, but it is also possible to create higher silanes and thus doubly upstage Stock. On the other hand, the isolation of the higher silanes using the cumbersome Stock process was Fehér's own original idea. Perhaps he might consider that he was now being derided. After all, I had managed everything without any great expense, simply by using a simple glass test tube. Fifteen years of effort, dozens of scientists, the struggle for funds – and now along comes this Plichta with his glass wool, which, moreover, also consists of silicon.

I made him an offer. 'Professor, we could put this pyrolytic work in the bottom drawer and take it out only when the higher silanes have been fractioned from the raw material.'

'Are you trying to add insult to injury after all that you've done to me?', he groaned. 'Please go away. I would like to be alone.'

My preparatory experiments continued to be successful. I finally also managed to synthesise dibromine-diphenyl-digermanium. This compound is the precise stereochemical (ie spatial) counterpart of those disilanes whose two asymmetrical silicon atoms had caused the plotter in the nuclear spectrograph to tremble when registering the proton signals.

$$
\begin{array}{ccc}
| & & | \\
H — Ge^* & — & Ge^* — H \\
| & & |
\end{array}
$$

This trembling ought now to be repeated when the digermaniums were measured. Several chemists were standing in front of the apparatus in great expectation, their eyes fixed on the plotter. As far as they were concerned, this would be conclusive proof of a new chemical compound. I, on the other hand, once more felt the icy breath at the back of my neck which always returns at decisive moments in my life. Stereochemists deal with spatial chemical structures, whereas I had long since been attempting to transfer a discovery from stereochemistry to the areas of mathematics, the science of numbers and space. My discovery could in principle not have been made by any mathematician alone.

A short time later we were able to repeat the measurement with a newly acquired high-resolution nuclear spectrograph. This time the plotter registered two wonderful independent signals.

So there had been no 'dirt' in the silicon compound after all! How embarrassing for the professors of organic and inorganic chemistry. From a stereochemical point of view, precisely the same applied for silicon and germanium atoms as for carbon atoms. The world's leading periodicals in inorganic chemistry would publish my findings. The actual significance of this, however, I would keep to myself for the time being.

The published article in the *Journal of the American Association of Chemists* shows the plotter recordings (spectra) of the stereochemical disilane and digermanium compounds beside each other. In the case of digermanium, however, the high-resolution signal is projected into the picture on the right as a microscopic photograph. When I took the journal into my hands I knew that I was on my way to solving two puzzles.

The first puzzle involved the geometry of the space around the atomic nucleus. Physicists have dealt with this space using three-dimensional mathematics. But what else could they use? Was any other notion of space available? Perhaps the curious space-time continuum with which they described the cosmology of the universe?

If space around an atomic nucleus, or, even better, around a point of finite size, were spherical but limited in some way – whether in a millionth fraction of a millimetre or in millions of light years – it would in either case be three-dimensional. Space around a point of finite size is, however, not finite but always infinite. And this is where my criticism arose. An infinite space cannot be three-dimensional, just as a infinite space always must be, regardless of its size. But which dimensions does it have, then? When two asymmetrical atoms occur opposite each other, there are a total of four mirror forms. This is necessitated by cruciform geometry which I illustrated using the example of the table set for two. I was certainly on a very hot trail here – one that would nonetheless lead me into a labyrinth. From the initial formulation of the puzzle in the summer of 1970 until its ultimate resolution, a total of 19 years would pass.

The second puzzle was much simpler, but did finally turn out to be the assignment of a lifetime. It involved the simple question: What is the best application for the silicon diesel oils? Very shortly I was at least able to establish that their use would have to involve combustion. I knew, of course, that they would be highly combustible in air, but no more. To resolve this question would take even longer than the first to solve: a total of 24 years.

At the beginning of the summer I worked out a series of processes elegantly substituting or linking silane and germanium compounds. By now I could easily have forced the hands of Professor Fehér and his successor, Professor Baudler, by applying for my qualification with a summary of my work or simply by making a dozen publications.

My superior received a visit from a colleague of his, the inorganic chemist Professor Hieber from Munich. I was asked to present the higher silanes to the guest and Frau Baudler.

I appeared with a beaker full of glass test tubes, the tops of which I had sealed with insulin caps. Not knowing what else to do, the three people present apart from myself could not but take the individually labelled test tubes and pass them around from hand to hand. But then something unusual happened. My superior had lit himself a cigar, as he was wont to do every few minutes. My eyes were captivated by the glow of the cigar. I took one of the test tubes and removed the rubber cap. Total silence immediately fell in the room. I held the open test tube in my right hand and smiled. All their attention was directed to what I was doing, as I slowly poured the contents of the glass

81

into an ashtray. It was fully transparent oil with the consistency of a vegetable oil. The three had expected that the oil would burn with a spurt of flame as soon as it came into contact with the air. Only I, the fourth in the room, was aware of something which all this time I had not even told Professor Fehér. From the heptasilanes (seven silicon atoms) on, the silanes are no longer automatically combustible.

Silence reigned for about half a minute. Professor Hieber had realized by now that something unexpected lay behind my presentation.

'But they aren't burning! Are they really silanes?'

Instead of replying I took a match, lit it, and brought the flame close to the oil. The silence was unreal. There was suddenly a flash of the kind only silanes can make. This was followed by the appearance of the yellow-brown glassy precipitate silicon monoxide. The deathly silence continued. Again it was Professor Hieber who was the first to realize just what had been seen. The textbooks said that high silanes cannot exist because they are unstable. In reality the oil becomes easier and safer to use as the length of the chains increases.

The guest leapt from his chair. He, who had lost an arm in an explosion, walked up to me and shook my hand.

'Dr Plichta, that's the most impressive thing I've ever seen or experienced in all my life. I can predict with the utmost confidence that you are going to go far. I wish you the very best for the future!'

I made a short bow and left the room.

Once outside, I leaned against the wall and tried to get my breath back to normal. I had not been able to tell the three observers what I had immediately realized the moment I lit the silane oil. This oil is not a precious new compound which chemists should keep for themselves and under no conditions simply ignite. No, the essence of this substance is in the secret of its ignition. It does not only exist so that it can be kept imprisoned in a small tube or used to form compounds with other elements. Its purpose is the power of the lightning with which it burns.

Professor Herr was invited by NASA to Texas. A former pupil of Otto Hahn, he was the only German chemist to receive some moondust from the first flight to the Moon. He was given one thimbleful. Because he appreciated my work I was summoned to his laboratory immediately on his return. I grabbed my camera and walked over to the nuclear chemistry building. The black sand appeared under stereochemical tests to be made of crystal pellets. I took some of these on the tip of my finger, held it high and asked: 'Professor Herr, how old is this stuff anyway?'

'This sand is 4.6 thousand million years old,' he replied. 'It is as old as the Earth.'

'And do we now know where the Moon comes from?'

He replied that we did not, and added: 'Once we have analysed this moondust we may know a bit more than we know now!'

When I was again standing outside, I looked into the evening sky and said aloud, 'But what does the Moon mean to me anyway?'

Suddenly I understood that the big question I had been trying to solve must have something to do with the Moon. If the Earth and Moon had a common origin, they should in fact be considered together as a double planet, despite their many differences. If astronauts were ever rocketed a few million kilometres into space, they would see from that perspective that we actually live on a double planet. This phenomenon is unique among the silicate planets, for Mercury, Venus and Mars do not have moons. Only the heavy gas planets have captured moons.[2] My mind was full of confusion. Why should I hurt my head worrying about the Moon?

I suddenly interrupted my qualifying in chemistry. The written admission examination for the PhD in law – because I had already got a degree I did not need to sit the state exams – no longer held any attraction for me. Instead, I took six months off in order to think. During this time one of my interests was the Japanese language. Because I was fascinated by the utter strangeness of this language I decided to attend an intensive language course.

I now sat from morning to evening in a lecture hall learning Japanese characters, the pictograms originally adopted from the Chinese writing system. Japanese does not have our grammar, particularly our way of conjugating the verb in person, number, tense, voice and mood. But this is not all that I found so interesting. My awakened interest in the number of consonants brought me inevitably to the Japanese consonantal alphabet. It is identical with our alphabet. One major difference is that the Japanese with their syllable characters always link a consonantal to one of the five vowels, as in ka, ke, ki, ko, ku, or pa, pe, pi, po, pu.

The teacher discussed human languages in general, and I soon got the feeling that I had also been drawn to this branch of science only to discover to my great amazement a new aspect of the triplicate. The brothers August Wilhelm and Friedrich von Schlegel actually demonstrated in the 19th century that there are three major types of languages on this Earth:

> isolating languages – eg Chinese
> agglutinative languages – eg Turkish
> inflected or fusional languages – eg Latin

There are thus three possibilities of grammatical expression. The mixture of races and their enormous variety of linguistic dialects has presented linguists with an enormous field of research that has turned them into 'specialists'. The notorious phrase 'Yes, but' immediately makes its appearance in their discourses. Any unusual feature of the most obscure Indian tribe is considered more important than this rule of three.

During the lesson, I asked our teacher: 'The rule of three occurs with conspicuous frequency in the natural sciences. Has anyone ever found out why there happen to be exactly three grammatical groups?' As I had expected, my question met with total incomprehension.

I next turned my attention to the question of human writing systems. Whereas European languages use letters to indicate sounds that make up syllables and words, the Chinese use a different character for every word of the language, even though each character (ideograph) may be pronounced in a totally different way from dialect to dialect. Although the Japanese are also an Asian people, they write as the Europeans do with signs representing sounds, but use Chinese characters to write them. The characters are pronounced completely differently from word to word and, in contrast to Chinese, no longer have a fixed meaning in themselves.

These rather confusing three types of writing led me onto

consider the three human races. A false notion of racial sensitivities has tended to deflect attention from the three basic races and to focus on the 32 mixed races of the world and their various peculiarities. This tendency has prevented a serious examination of the three main races that exist on this planet –

Negroid
Mongoloid
Caucasian

– all of whom have their origin in Asia. According to the triple-dispersion theory of Professor Egon Eickstedt, the Negroid races originate in southern Asia, the Mongoloid in eastern Asia, and the Europeans (Caucasians) in north-west Eurasia. (American Indians are a branch of the Mongoloid peoples.)

Because I was aware that many people of Negroid race are to be found in southern India, in New Guinea and in certain Pacific islands, I immediately saw the plausibility of the dispersion theory for the black population of Africa undoubtedly did not make their way to southern Asia by land or on wooden rafts. The peoples of Africa migrated from Asia at some time in the distant past. However, the existence in Africa of aboriginal races from the time before the ice ages, such as the Pygmies, means that scientific indifference has again been victorious.

I then began to feel anger at palaeontologists and their celebrated fossil-bone discoveries, for all the remains they dig up from the time before the fourth and final ice age relate to extinct human races which were only forerunners of the three races that exist today.

My studies in prehistory also uncovered an unexpected triplicate to do with the original economic structures prevailing in all three races:

hunting
tilling the soil
animal husbandry

My studies of zoology, anatomy and physiology led to such an enormous amount of evidence of the three-fold order of existence that I was no longer happy to be in the laboratory. The silane oils for which I would later receive a patent, and which according to chemistry textbooks should not exist at all, were turning out to be not simply a scientific oversight that I had uncovered but rather a tripwire of divine origin by which I would fully realize how thoroughly scientists can lie by omission or silence, or by confident assertion when they are sure that such assertions cannot be refuted very easily.

Until then I had believed in the emergence of the first forms of life through random processes and also in Darwin's teachings on the origins of species through natural selection. I now began to have my doubts.

Because we now know that the transition from ape to human was not a gradual process – and we know that by the different numbers of chromosomes in the cells of each species – the theory of the evolution of humans and apes from a common ancestor is not without a certain audacity. Nobody tells our children and students that the females of the three anthropoid apes – the gorillas, orang-utans and chimpanzees – do not have a clitoris. This fact is not hushed up because of any misplaced puritanism. It is ignored because it does not fit into the theory of evolution. The occurrence of this part of the female anatomy in humans had far-reaching consequences and cannot have evolved by coincidence.

My thoughts then turned once more to theoretical physics. In this science coincidence has been accorded the status of a demi-god. Scientists long wished to remove God as Creator and Prime Mover from physics because no God can be proved to exist using scientific methods. From the – so apparent – coincidence of all processes in the electron cloud it was rashly inferred that all processes in the universe were caused by coincidence. A comfortable substitute had thus been found for God. From the natural constants to the human mind – everything is a coincidence. It was in refutation of this assertion that Einstein once stated, 'God does not play dice.'

Although the apparition in my bedroom that night and the prophecy of Professor Hauser were constantly in my mind, I began to realize why I should nevertheless not study theoretical physics. No person can study this subject when from the outset he has such strong doubts. The student would either fail to pass his exams or be declared 'insane'. Even a self-taught approach would also be unsuccessful because, if our notions of the atomic nucleus and the electron cloud are wrong, it would then be impossible for me to discover the true basis of matter by studying obsolete and erroneous theories. Whoever wants to get to the bottom of the secret contained in the Planck-Einstein equation and wishes to subject an existing science to a rigorous process of renewal on the foundation of a sound basis – and not a foundation invented by the fertile minds of physicists – has to proceed without any possibility of misdirection.

If I was genuinely predestined to discover the principles by which the world is governed, there would therefore have to be a reason why I was so committed to chemistry. Even as a child I had wanted to educate myself solely in that science. Now, after my university studies, when I was finally free from impending examinations, I realized that I had not studied the subject thoroughly enough. Chemistry comprises such a vast body of knowledge that it can safely be said that no chemist today has total command of the subject. So what should I do now?

In the autumn of 1971 I finally took up employment in the chemical industry. My duties there seemed all too easy. I almost had the feeling that a 'good fairy' was looking after me and helping me on. After only two years, when I was 33 years old, the chairman of the firm I was working for informed me that I was to be offered a position on the board of directors in a further two years' time. Instead of gratefully accepting this offer-in-waiting I asked for a week to consider the matter.

NOTES
1 Thermal decomposition of chemical compounds which – in the case of chain hydrocarbons – produce important isomers (branched chains). One feature of these isomers is that they possess higher octane rates than the materials of which they are composed.
2 Phobos and Deimos, the satellites referred to as the moons of Mars, are irregularly-formed captured meteorites with a maximum diameter of only 12 and 27 kilometres respectively.

CHAPTER EIGHT

UPSIDE-DOWN AND BACKWARDS

Before I started working in the chemical industry I had generally considered pharmacology to be nothing more than a branch of chemistry. In the course of my work I perceived that for its international business activities the company for which I worked really needed a chemist who was at the same time a pharmacologist. Many of the ingredients that go into cosmetics are pharmaceutical substances.

As it was now clear that I would still have to wait two years for the coveted position on the board, the idea came to me to use the time to study for the national exam in pharmacology. This would be of considerable advantage to the firm, and far better than recruiting an additional pharmacist. For me the advantage was also clear – it was an opportunity to broaden my knowledge of biochemistry and pharmaceutical chemistry.

In the week allotted me to make my decision, I phoned my brother. He had in the meantime become as rich as he had always dreamed, had passed the school-leaving certificate, and was studying medicine.

He took a flight to Düsseldorf and on his arrival at our house was as serious as ever. My brother, Helga and I went into our sitting-room. I sat on the sofa while Paul, who was clearly agitated, would not sit down.

Some yards in front of me, Helga was standing at the table and began, full of pride,

'Peter is going to be a member of the board in a couple of years!'

Paul strode over to the table and cut in abruptly, 'Peter isn't going to join the board. He must leave the company at once. My studies of medicine at the university are not going as well as I had hoped. Peter has to study medicine with me and help me in my studies. You know I just can't afford to let my studies drift now!'

'Paul, my studying medicine would not be the right way to go about it. Let me study pharmacology. Then I will be better able to help you.'

Paul was obviously relieved.

'Study pharmacology then – that's OK with me. But without your help I'll never be able to pass the preliminary examinations.'

Helga interrupted him. 'Have both of you lost your senses? Peter has a great future ahead of him in business. What is a degree in pharmacology compared to the prospects in store for him now? Do you imagine he is going to sell cough medicine in a pharmacy to the man in the street?'

'But if Peter becomes a pharmacist, I'll be able to give him a pharmacy as a present after he finishes his exams. He has always wanted a place where he could study. He would then be able to have a quiet office over the pharmacy where he could work as a theoretician, while down below his employees could sell the cough mixture.'

My heart was beating fast. I was astonished that my brother should have come up with such a good idea.

'No, no, no,' Helga snarled at him. 'A pharmacist today is no longer what it used to be. Today you need a few doctors' surgeries over the pharmacy if it is to be a success.'

This was the moment of Paul's victory. He had only to ask: 'How much money do you need then?'

In false triumph Helga thought of a number that should have made Paul turn pale: 'One and a half million marks!'

But Paul was clearly relieved to have got off so lightly. He knew exactly how important it was that his brother helped him.

'I hereby promise that the day I am a doctor and my brother a pharmacist, Peter will receive from me one and a half million marks for a building to contain doctors' surgeries and a pharmacy.'

Helga walked up to Paul: 'Raise your hand and swear it!'

Paul raised his hand, looked at Helga, and said, 'I swear it!'

I sat looking at them in silence. The fact that my brother was willing to part with his legendary riches only showed the difficulty he was in. So Paul was to become a doctor and I a pharmacist. As a pharmacist with my own pharmacy I would be free. That would be the greater advantage to me, not the money. Membership of the board of a chemical corporation would have given me the same financial security, but would scarcely have given me the time or opportunity to think about the riddle of the universe. I made my decision accordingly.

As a place to study I chose Marburg. This city at that time was the main citadel of German pharmacology and the chief commander of the citadel was Professor Böhme who held a teaching post there. He had been awarded at least a dozen honorary doctorates from the most prestigious German universities. In collaboration with Professor Hardke, he is author of the critical text of the Seventh *German Pharmacopoeia* (with which German pharmacology finally emerged from the medieval conditions of the Sixth *German Pharmacopoeia*). After a personal visit to Professor Böhme I managed to get myself accepted into the fourth semester – although I undertook a series of vain attempts in other directions.

Because the pharmacology course is generally much too short for 'normal' students, a frenetic teaching process is required to instil everything a future pharmacist should really know. This can lead to frustration and uncertainty, and for many people is a direct continuation of their unsatisfactory experience of secondary schools. In our schools, an abundance of material is crammed into the pupils' heads, and nobody seems to care that most of this knowledge is forgotten immediately after the exams. This is the exact reverse of the maxim *non scholae sed vitae* ([we learn] not for school but for life).

How can young people be expected to learn to recognize connections and correspondences between different aspects of their knowledge, and to pose the question 'Why?', when natural and God-given curiosity – which is present in all young people – is not supported and strengthened?

My situation as a student in Marburg was not comparable with that of other pharmacology students, for I had already passed through the entire university system once before. Moreover, by virtue of my sojourn in a commercial enterprise, I had acquired a certain healthy dissociation from academia. I now noticed that my experience and my objectivity in relation to the subject meant that I was no longer prepared to ignore my search for interconnections, nor merely cram in unconnected and superficial pieces of information for the next exam.

Pharmacology is a subject that merges major parts of the three natural sciences – **chemistry, physics and biology** – into an independent science. In addition, pharmacology is the twin sister of medicine. The subject of health and sickness is of basic concern to everybody. It is therefore a prime example of the need for holistic thinking.

I nevertheless devoted my determined energies to cramming.

After my wife Helga and I had separated before I started at the university, I was fortunate to meet a young lady who was studying at the same course. Ingrid had a natural talent for biology (particularly botany), and I gave her some help with my knowledge of physics and chemistry.

Because my physics textbook had totally fallen to pieces through overuse, I bought a new edition. It contained a chapter that had recently been added on statistical physics – and I was soon spellbound by this subject.

The chapter dealt with the 'statistics of groups' and 'physical groups' and began as follows:

> A herd of apes has discovered an enormous sack full of letter cookies and each ape is having a lot of fun lining up the letters that he has randomly taken out one after the other to form 'text'. The sack also contains word separators (spaces). Could Hamlet's monologue, or at least the phrase 'TO BE OR NOT TO BE', ever be created by such a process?

The author of this chapter, Dr Helmut Vogel, was at that time working at a research institute for biophysics or biochemistry. His quotation from *Hamlet* was aimed at the crazy idea of transferring the unqualified coincidence at the basis of quantum mechanics to the sciences of chemistry and biology. Behind the activity of the apes composing random text there is the question of whether life could ever have arisen from the 'primordial soup'. At that time attempts were being made, starting with the

91

principles of physics, to present the chemistry of peptides (the building-blocks of protein) in all living beings as the sum of random processes of creation. Because of the authority wielded by Greater Physics no construction plan but only pure coincidence was admitted as the origin of life itself. The number of amino acids – precisely 20 – must therefore also be a coincidence. But because I happened to be on a course studying biochemistry and was obliged to come to grips with the chemistry of these amino acids, I was riveted by this discovery.

If apes were able to toss out *Hamlet* by chance, no building plan was needed at all. I suddenly realized that if there was even a possibility that nature had been influenced by random events, it would never have produced the miracle of the human mind. Instead, there would have been too many false developments which would have accumulated and finally blocked the progress of life. Moreover, the stereochemical building-blocks of life are spatially arranged components and not just biscuits that can be simply laid alongside each other. The origin of life can therefore not be explained by linear random chains, but only by exponential – ie spatial – structure. And that is precisely what the proponents of quantum mechanics – because of their lack of knowledge in stereochemistry – have failed to understand from the very outset.

This brought me once again back to the fundamental question of nature. It was becoming increasingly clear to me that the same natural law must be at the foundation of all three natural sciences. And the plan must have been based on number theory because I was constantly encountering the same numbers.

This means that no such thing as coincidence in the real sense can exist at all.

I had formerly only been interested in the 20 amino acids from which all life is composed because of the curious division of 1 and 19 observed in their rotatory characteristics. But now when I examined their chemical diagrams in a textbook of biochemistry[1] I noticed that the artist had clearly illustrated the asymmetry of the 19 centres by indicating the four connecting arms. Among the 19 left-oriented amino acids, there are two that each have a second asymmetrical centre.

The artist had also illustrated this feature for l-threonine:

$$\begin{array}{ccc} | & & | \\ H - C^* & - & C^* - H \\ | & & | \end{array}$$

In the case of l-isoleucine, however, the connecting arm to one of the hydrogen atoms is not drawn. The asymmetry of the second carbon atom cannot be recognized at all:

$$\begin{array}{ccc} | & & | \\ HC & - & C^* - H \\ | & & | \end{array}$$

This textbook, which has been used to impart the fundamentals of biochemistry to a whole generation of doctors and pharmacologists, does not deal with the two optical centres in isoleucine. The significance of the question of why two of the 19 left-oriented amino acids have doubled asymmetrical centres has been lost on the elite of the biochemistry world.

Surely it is also rather superficial from a stereochemical point of view for scientists to speak of 19 left-oriented amino acids when 17 amino acids have one stereochemical carbon atom and only the left-oriented form exists in nature. The two amino acids with two stereochemical centres each have four mirrored forms.

Scientific opinion assumes that a (racemic) mixture of left- and right-oriented forms must have existed in the primordial soup. Because we do not know where the right mirrored form disappeared to, it is now postulated that the combinatory ratio of mirrored forms is not exactly 50:50, but only 51:49. In the course of evolution, the two mirrored forms are then supposed to have obliterated each other, so that the extra 2 per cent now remain for the left mirrored form.

The matrixes which were later composed for the production of peptides were therefore programmed for the left mirrored form.

The mythical Baron von Münchhausen would have shrieked with delight.

The whole theory collapses because of the two amino acids with the doubled mirror centres – which means that in the primordial soup four lower forms must have existed for the amino acid threonine and these forms were made up of two families – threonine and allothreonine. Two mirrored forms exist from each of the two families. They are both capable of devouring each other, which would leave two (left) forms remaining. Because three mirrored forms have disappeared, however, the theory is untenable.

The stereochemical twin atomic disilane that was so important for me in Cologne has the same chemical framework as l-isoleucine and l-threonine.

$$H — \overset{\displaystyle |}{\underset{\displaystyle |}{Si^*}} — \overset{\displaystyle |}{\underset{\displaystyle |}{Si^*}} — H$$

The only difference is that the structural formula for the two amino acids has four-armed carbon atoms as stereochemical atoms (C instead of Si).

I only noticed this because Professor Karlson had forgotten to include a black stroke between a hydrogen atom and a carbon atom.

For the first time I perceived some small intimation of the connection between my work in Cologne on the 19 stereochemical amino acids and the 19 pure isotopes with uneven atomic numbers.

I told Ingrid of my experience in Cologne, and about my conviction that I was destined to find out why life had happened to decide on 1 + 19 amino acids.

She was flabbergasted. 'But what are you doing here in Marburg studying pharmacy?'

'Studying pharmacy seems to have a certain significance for me, for some reason I do not yet know. But I believe I will know before I am finished.'

I then gave her a fairly drastic account of what I thought of my fellow scientists. 'They are satisfied with everything they can measure with their instruments. They are used to seeing nature as it appears to them. The notion that there is something mysterious under the surface is totally foreign to them. Matter, all that our universe is made up of, for them is sterile and dead. The fact that living organisms exist at all is due, in their opinion, to chance and to carbon's peculiar tendency to form beautiful organic compounds, which they entirely take for granted.'

'Yes, but do you think the riddle of the universe is a secret that *can* be discovered?'

'Ingrid, I know for certain that one day I'll discover something of enormous importance.'

'And what will you do then?'

'It is probably just as difficult to get public attention for something really new as it is to discover it in the first place. When the truth is finally discovered and this discovery shows that all we have achieved so far has been wrong, the new facts cannot simply be published – certainly not at a time when scientists are constantly publishing as if there were no tomorrow. You just can't imagine how angry they would be if someone turned up and started pointing the finger at their hopeless deficiencies in matters of profound importance. They feel good in a world where truth remains hidden. In such a world anybody can claim what he wants, provided he is not a revolutionary and provided nobody can prove the contrary. Revolutions are always accepted as having been necessary only after they have succeeded. You only have to have a thorough knowledge of the history of science to realize that it has been one vast human tragedy all along.

'If it turns out that my suspicions of the existence of a construction plan for creation are well founded, I won't be able to publish it just like that. Nobody would ever take me seriously. Nobody would help me, either. I would have to furnish the entire proof myself. But even if I managed it, my colleagues would only glance in my direction to show me how crazy they think I am.

'If the physics of the future can be reduced to very simple numeric connections, the entire body of natural science will collapse like a house of cards. Such new theories would be most dangerous for those who are professionally involved with numbers: mathematicians. They deny that numbers exist at all. For them numbers are products of the human imagination. They maintain that scientists only imagine that they recognize natural constants. That is the comfortable solution.'

Ingrid was fascinated. 'And how do you propose to do it? How do you start trying to discover anything? What are you looking for at the moment?'

'We have just done the structure of red blood corpuscles as preparation for our next test. You know that in Karlson's book

95

there is no solution to the problem of how the inhaled oxygen is held by the red corpuscles. He only talks of a coordination compound in which five coordination points are occupied by nitrogen and the sixth coordination point is occupied by an oxygen instead of a nitrogen molecule. Nobody knows how the oxygen molecule is held by the iron atom, although the molecular structure of the red corpuscles has been deciphered. Four iron atoms have been found, four porphyrine residuals and four peptide chains, whose amino acid sequence has been deciphered. Everything is known about how blood brings oxygen from the air to the individual cells. Pure oxygen is actually pure poison for organic compounds. It destroys everything. But somehow the red blood corpuscles manage to protect themselves from the oxygen.

The structure formula of haeme which may appear rather complex, is in fact an ingenious ring system of carbon and nitrogen atoms of which the double-bond electrons are freely mobile and can thus have a circular orbit.

$$N \qquad N$$
$$\bullet$$
$$N \qquad N$$

Four nitrogen atoms are located at the centre of this ring structure. These hold a central freely-mobile iron atom in the middle. The iron atom (indicated in the diagram by a spot) is thus surrounded by four nitrogen atoms. The iron atom is therefore considered to be simply a central ligand which simply drops out of the primeval soup.'

Ingrid interrupted me: 'And what do you think?'

'Ever since I saw the picture of the oxygen bonding curve in Karlson's book, I have had my suspicions. The curve is sigmoid. I have seen such S-shaped curves once before in a textbook, in a chapter dealing with ferromagnetism. Actually, one of the astonishing features of iron is that it can magnify the magnetic field of a coil which surrounds it by several hundred per cent. The magnetization curves are referred to in physics as hysteris loops.

'I rather think that the iron in haemoglobin has a ferromagnetic function. This suspicion was strengthened when

I counted the double bonds in haeme molecules. There are 13 double bonds and therefore 26 mobile electrons.'

'And why is that so important?'

'Ingrid, iron just happens to be the twenty-sixth element which also means that its atomic nucleus is surrounded by 26 electrons. This could mean that iron in the blood is not a bivalent ligand at all, but is, in fact, a zerovalent metal atom. The chemist who deciphered the structure of haeme was not aware of any organic molecules with zerovalent metal atoms. The same can be said of the chemist who worked out the sequence of the four peptide chains.

'I once synthesized a compound the structure of which looks like a sandwich and that has a zerovalent chromium atom in the centre. This chromium atom is held in a freely mobile state only by rotating double-bond electrons of the benzene rings. A benzene ring has six rotating electrons, and a zerovalent chromium atom contains six electrons on its third and fourth shells with which it can form bonds.'

'This information should be published,' said Ingrid.

'Yes, it could be published all right. The only problem is that I don't know what sort of trick the giant molecule uses to receive oxygen in the lungs so elegantly and to again release it after it has been used.'

I was finally to find the solution in 1981. The double-bond electrons orbiting in circles through the molecule generate an electrical field of the type familiar to physicists or electricians that is produced by a circular conductor carrying a current. The four nitrogen atoms are in fact nothing other than the four poles of a quadrupole magnet.

Quadrupole magnets are used in nuclear physics to focus beam transport systems. With the juxtaposition of north poles (symbol N) and south poles (symbol S) in planar arrangement, a concentration of the nuclear particles at the central point of the quadrupole magnet is maintained.

The ferromagnetic effect of a central iron atom with a zero charge on a magnetic field is that the entire molecule with its four haeme groups behaves like an iron magnet. When a paramagnetic material approaches this molecule, it will be affected by the magnetic force. The protein shell with its four chains can manage to switch such a magnet on and off by having its spatial arrangement changed through pH shifts. One of the four gases we breathe – oxygen – is paramagnetic (magnetic). The other three gases in the atmosphere – **nitrogen, argon** and **carbon dioxide** – are diamagnetic (non-magnetic). Knowledge of the paramagnetic character of oxygen is assumed in examinations for chemistry and physics. Biologists, however, are totally unaware of this phenomenon. Because no ferromagnetic phenomena appear in the chemistry of life, the biologists do not have to worry about it. A more elegant bond than the molecular-physical bond[2] described here is inconceivable. This notion is supported by the fact that one of the most poisonous gases, carbon monoxide, is known to form more fixed compounds with haemoglobin. This gas is also paramagnetic.

The resistance to such a simple solution is, as always, based on the novelty of the concept, as well as on the dogma that oxygen transport must 'somehow' be a chemical and not an electrophysical phenomenon.

I entered my name for the second national examination in the spring of 1976. Because I had already got into trouble with several of my professors I was not unduly surprised when I received prior notification to the effect that my failure had already been decided. To avoid this trap I requested an appointment with Professor Böhme, the president of the Hesse state examining board.

I placed my fate in his hands by offering to change university. I said I would prefer to start studying again rather than fail in any field of chemistry, so great was my love for the subject.

My request seemed to move the professor. 'Mr Plichta, I would prefer that you did not change university and that you register for the second national examination here. I shall think of some way to resolve this problem, but first of all I'll have to listen to the arguments from the other side. But don't worry: I'll find a solution.'

I stood in front of his office door and had a premonition that I would soon discover why I had decided to study pharmacology in Marburg.

Some weeks later, a notice appeared on the Institute's noticeboard:

State Examination Board of Hesse
Director: Professor Dr hc Böhme

The examination of Dr Plichta in pharmaceutical chemistry will be undertaken by Professor Böhme.

signed: Professor Dr hc Böhme

I knew that this would be the most challenging and difficult examination of my life. Because of his age and the range of his interests, Professor Böhme only tested exam candidates in exceptional cases. My examination therefore became something special for the whole institute.

I knew that Professor Böhme would be very tough but fair in the examination. He was the author of the critical texts on the European pharmaceutical textbooks that were then being prepared. He was therefore intimately familiar with all the pharmaceutical problems in the world, and also knew every detail of their legal and historical peculiarities.

On the day of the examination I appeared in the Institute with some time to spare. As if driven by a premonition, I stepped into a laboratory in which I had never been before. Apart from me, the room was completely empty.

On one of the tiled laboratory tables lay a big red book – the critical text on the Seventh *German Pharmacopoeia* by Böhme and Hartke. This book had over a thousand pages and it would have been pointless to glance at it now. Nevertheless I took the volume into my hands, lifted it with outstretched arms up to the level of my eye and let it fall back onto the table, so that it opened by itself. I had never before tried this rather curious way of consulting the oracle.

At the top of the page on the right I read the name of the drug ephedrine. Below this was an illustration of its molecular structure.

Ephedrine is related to those disilane and digermanium molecules with which I had worked in Cologne. So there they were again, the stereochemical twin atoms. Exactly like the two amino acids, the ephedrine molecule consists of two stereochemical carbon atoms, each of which has one free hydrogen atom:

$$H - C^* - C^* - H$$

I was filled with curiosity and read several pages of the textbook and came across the very complex problem of racemic separation (separation of the four symmetrical forms) in the technical synthesis of ephedrine. I became annoyed. I had never heard of this before. If I was asked even one question relating to such a difficult problem at the beginning of my test, I would be finished. If twin atoms had not been so important to me, I would not even have glanced at Herr Böhme's commentary.

But the time had now come. I closed the thick volume, walked into the examination hall and sat down at Professor Böhme's desk.

Three heavy volumes were lying on the desk. Professor Böhme hesitated a moment and selected the book in the middle – it was the critical text on the Seventh *German Pharmacopoeia*. Exactly as I had done just a short time before, he raised the book with two outstretched arms, up to the level of his eyes and let it fall again. The book hit the desk and lay there open. Even while he was bending down to read the page, I recognised the formula with the asymmetrical twin atoms. This time I was reading it upside-down and backwards.

'Mr Plichta, ephedrine synthesis!' ordered Professor Böhme with a wave of his hand.

I did not dare turn around even though I felt as if someone was standing behind me.

This was the only time in my life that I was really tested in chemistry and pharmacology. It was a veritable exchange of blows. It all boiled down to whether there was one single question that I could not answer, one single word that I did not know. The difficult first question paved the way for what was to come. I spoke and explained as best I could. Each sentence I spoke was chosen for its clarity: I chose each word not only for its communicative power but also for its beauty. This was my contribution to the play that was now being performed in the room. I was at last sitting in front of the famous Professor Böhme and was finally aware that I had come to Marburg to study pharmacology just for this day. The two asymmetrical twin atoms had been around for millennia.

Professor Böhme only asked questions which I knew about and about which an ordinary student of pharmacology could not know much, but which had been of significance to me and occupied my mind at some time in my life. He tested me in every branch of pharmacology. I listened to myself speak and was fascinated and full of awe. I now understood that the many unusual events in my life had not been coincidence but only different stages in the journey towards one final goal. It had all begun when I had decided in Cologne to make a preparation of the first silicon hydride compound with two asymmetrical twin atoms. The examination went on for half an hour, one hour, one and a half hours and finally Professor Böhme noticed that the exam duration had long passed. The two of us sat there, totally exhausted.

The old giant of a man smote his fist down on the table. He leapt to his feet and his chair turned over with a crash and landed a few yards away. He reached across the table and offered me his hand.

'Dr Plichta, that was an experience!' he thundered as we shook hands.

1 Peter Karlson, *Biochemie für Mediziner und Naturwissenschaftler*, Stuttgart, 8th edition, 1972.
2 Some iron atoms – as occur, for instance, in vaporized iron – are paramagnetic. Ferromagnetism is always linked to structures. In the haemoglobin molecule, the four haeme groups with their four iron atoms have a precise spatial arrangement.

CHAPTER NINE

THE QUEEN OF THE SCIENCES

Because it was going to take my brother Paul a few more years to become a doctor, I had originally chosen to study in Marburg with the intention of becoming a doctor in medical biology. During this time I thought Ingrid would be able to earn enough money as a pharmacist to support the two of us.

After my success in the examination I decided to change plans, to move back to Düsseldorf, and to find myself a job as an assistant in a pharmacy.

At the age of 30 my plan was to work until my fortieth year before retiring for at least ten years to devote myself entirely to research and thinking. I was now 36 years old. I would need one further year before I could apply for a pharmacist's licence. But it was during this year that Helga died – Helga from whom I had in the meantime been divorced. Her death fulfilled half of the prophecy I had never forgotten. Although I had foreseen her early death, the shock was nevertheless very hard indeed, and there was nobody to whom I could turn for comfort. The other half of the prophecy was that I would one day solve the puzzle of the most fundamental physical constants and thus one of nature's great secrets.

The period of loneliness which now began was alleviated only by the presence of my five-year-old daughter. A second marriage was little more than a refuge for me and did not last three years.

I did not go to my brother to seek the money for the pharmacy. I outflanked him by going to his mother-in-law and telling her of his promise to Helga. It would cost DM520,000 to purchase an apartment and a pharmacy with all the fittings. In addition, a sum of DM250,000 in gift tax had to be paid. I received the money and waived any claim to the other half of the promised DM1.5 million. The contract with Paul's mother-in-law made me financially independent. My plan to retire at the age of 40 looked as if it might come true after all.

While the pharmacy was being built at Sigmaringenstrasse 1, I had a year's time to occupy myself with astronomy and astrophysics.

The natural sciences made a leap from the middle ages into modern times with Isaac Newton's definition of the law of gravity, after Johannes Kepler had completed the groundwork with his three laws on the movement of planets. Until then nobody knew why the Earth continued to orbit the sun and did not fly off into space. The same applied to the Earth-Moon system. Newton proved that heavenly bodies are held together by a mysterious force, but had no qualms in admitting that nothing was known about what was behind this force. The situation has not changed since then. The law of attraction between the Earth and the Moon is a function of the mass of each celestial body and the distance between them. The term *radius* that is used in this context is the distance between the centre of the Earth and the centre of the Moon. The term is used because the Moon describes a circle around the Earth. Because the power of attraction decreases as the distance (radius) between the two heavenly bodies increases, the radius has a reciprocal effect $= 1/r$.

The numbers occurring under the line of a fraction in physical equations are generally not explained with sufficient clarity in secondary schools. The result can be seen in young people's lack of ability in abstract reasoning and their inbuilt resistance to formulas.

The radius is placed below the line in the fraction simply because the power decreases as the distance increases (the greater the number below the line, the smaller is the value of the fraction).

Because the radius between the Moon and the Earth is obviously the same as that between the Earth and the Moon, the two quotients $1/r$ are included in the law of gravity in the form of the product $1/r^2$. This fraction (1 divided by the square of the radius) is generally referred to as the reciprocal square law.

This law regulates all behaviour in empty space. If a source of light in the form of a point were to be calibrated with a photometer at a distance of one yard, this light metre would register only 25 per cent of the light when placed at a distance of two yards, and only 11 per cent at a distance of three yards. Why does the device show these percentage values? If two is given as a value for the variable r in the above equation, the result would be 1 divided by 2 to the power of 2, ie 1 divided by 4. If the value of r is 3, the value for the fraction would be 1 divided by 9. But 100 divided by 9 is 11 (with the remainder 1). The series can be continued in this way.

While I had understood the reciprocal square law so far only in the physical sense, I now began to suspect that merely understanding such an important law would not be sufficient. It is much more important to ask why physical effects in space generally weaken according to numbers to the power of two. It is a curious fact that the greatest physicist in the history of the world (Newton) and the greatest philosopher (Kant) allowed for God's possibility of fitting out the world with natural laws different from the ones we know. Kant speaks in this context about replacing the 'arbitrary' reciprocal square law (to the power of 2) by some other law, namely the cubic law (to the power of 3). Although I did not doubt Newton's or Kant's belief in God's omnipotence, I was a bit suspicious, and although no physicist today talks about the omnipotence of God, nothing has changed with regard to the apparent arbitrariness of natural laws.

Newton and Kant did not know that the number of electron pairs in the atomic 'shell' is limited. The maximum number of atomic pairs is, as we have seen, 1, 4, 9, 16 for the various electron orbits. On the innermost orbit around the atomic nucleus only one pair of electrons has place; a maximum of 4 pairs fit on the second level; 9 on the third; and 16 on the fourth. Because these four numbers are the squares of 1, 2, 3 and 4, the square law is therefore numerically anchored in the atom itself and therefore in the whole of nature.

In the course of my studies in astronomy and astrophysics I

had once more to look at the concepts of eternity and the finite. This time, however, I did not examine them in the context of numbers but in the context of space.

Before the Renaissance, which saw the rebirth of great classical thought, the idea of space was not given much attention. The notion of 'eternity' was only assigned to time. The German cardinal Nicolaus Cusanus (of Cusa on the River Mosel in Germany), lawyer, diplomat, philosopher and mathematician, was the first to realize that space can not be limited but is in fact infinite. He connected the infinity of space and time with the omnipotence of a personal God. Highly respected by his contemporaries, he was able to publish books containing his revolutionary ideas despite the Inquisition.

About one hundred years later, Giordano Bruno (from Nola near Naples) took up Cusanus' idea. Bruno, who was a mere monk, neither cardinal nor diplomat – although a courageous debater – took the contemporary dogma of the Church seriously to task and paid the price for it at the stake in the marketplace of Rome in the year 1600. According to the leaders of the Church, the Earth and the heavenly bodies (sun, Moon, wandering stars [planets] and fixed stars) were a closed system existing in a great sphere, behind which was what was then referred to as heaven (or paradise). But this heaven was also thought to be finite. The notion of infinitely empty space did not exist.

Bruno, who was well ahead of his time (not only in cosmology), realized that finite space differed from infinite space by a curious geometrical feature. A finite space, no matter how large it is, can have only one centre. An infinite space, on the other hand, has its centre everywhere – ie any point is its centre. Mathematically, infinite space has an infinite number of centres.

Leibniz, whose genius inevitably forced him to confront the problem of infinity, developed Bruno's idea one hundred years later in his great work *Monadologie* (*monás* is ancient Greek for 'unit'). It was still dangerous, however, to display an intellectual affinity with Bruno. Leibniz described the centres of infinity as 'monads'. Each single monad contains the reflection of the entire universe. His monads had no dimensions; in the opinion of Leibniz matter only 'adhered' to the monads. This is one reason he was opposed to the idea of atoms, a concept that was

105

supported at the time by his chief rival, Newton. In view of his assertion that these strange points, which Newton called atoms instead of monads, had to have substance in space, Newton was the more correct of the two. He, and all atomists after him (until today), unfortunately ceased to pursue the question of infinity when they reached these points. No atom was considered to be the centre of infinity.

Leibniz's theory of monads was therefore not registered in scientific consciousness at all at the time, and Newton's theory of atoms was contested until this century, above all by the elite of the scientific world.

One hundred years were to pass after the death of Leibniz before F. Heinrich Jacobi published excerpts from Bruno's old philosophical writings. Only then did these ideas come to have an influence on some of the greatest philosophers of the 19th century, F. W. J. Schelling and, of course, J. W. Goethe, whose universal mind strove towards infinity in the true Faustian sense.

Although in the 20th century the notion of atoms has again been explored – before being brought to its logical, or illogical, conclusion in a description of nature referred to as the 'particle zoo' – the search for a true definition of infinity has again faded into the background. Today our concept of space has again reached the point where it was in the middle ages: in a finite universe.

Because a purely reciprocal law of numbers is constantly at work in space, a physical effect, such as gravity or light, should also diminish with increasing distance and approach zero. It is a peculiar feature of infinity that it can be infinitely large as well as infinitely small.

Whereas the natural numbers begin with 1, 2, 3, 4, 5 ... and never end, the reciprocal numbers begin with 1/1, 1/2, 1/3, 1/4 ... and approach zero. The number 1 is therefore a frontier between the whole and the reciprocal numbers.

If the whole numbers are imagined as marked pearls on a string, it is easy to see that this string will never end.

The inversion of this concept, however, contains a notional difficulty. Because the difference between 1 and 2, and therefore the distance between two pearls, is exactly the same as the difference between 1 and 0, the reciprocal numbers (*infinitely* many), all fit into this *finite* distance regardless of how big a number is (for example, a number with a thousand million multiplied by a thousand million zeros). Its reciprocal number will always be larger than zero and, of course, smaller than 1.

Through my occupation with the infinitely large and infinitely small, something occurred to me that came as a great surprise. Relating a number, for example 3, and its reciprocal value 1/3 (= 0.3333...) is the quadratic factor 3^2. This relationship exists because 0.3333 ... must be multiplied by 9 to get the number 3 (0.3333 ... × 9 = 3). In the case of 4 and its reciprocal value 1/4, the quadratic factor is 16.

The quadratic factor that relates a number and its reciprocal value seemed to me an indication that the reciprocal square law as a law of space connects numbers and space. If the God of Newton and Kant was an architect and mathematician, as those two gentlemen would certainly have claimed, He would have had to stick to the rules of mathematics and logic. He would therefore not have accepted any element of chance in His plan of Creation.

The number 1, which I perceived as a frontier between the whole and the reciprocal numbers, assumes a very special significance. And when this number is examined more closely, some very curious features emerge. Whereas the roots of the uneven and non-quadratic numbers are irrational (eg the square root of 3 is 1.73205 ...), the square root of 1 is not an irrational number. It is the root of 1 = −1, and the root of −1 = i, an abbreviation for the word *imaginary*.

As I thus occupied myself with exploring the whole numbers and their reciprocal values, it became clear to me that I had finally reached the very foundation of mathematics in the number 1 and its structure.

When one day a wash-basin had to be installed in the bathroom of the pharmacy, and we concluded that there was only one corner where it could be installed, I asked the workmen to put in a triangular basin and hang two large mirrors above it lining the corner.

Each time I look in a normal mirror I am irritated because the man in it who keeps looking out at me does not really exist as I see him. I have the parting in my hair on the right side, and my reflection has it on his left. Most people do not bother about the difference; perhaps many people even believe that they really look like the person they see in the mirror.

In his book *Timaeus*, Plato describes a reflective surface consisting of two mirrors meeting at a right-angle. Such a mirror reverses its image in space and always gives three reflections. In the middle there is normally a solid black line, because the mirror surfaces at the point where they meet have not been ground at an angle of 45°.

After the workmen had finished the installation, I approached my new 'space mirror'. I saw Peter Plichta standing there looking like me, and he really looked as I do. The space mirror showed me as if I were standing in front of myself (and thus in reverse). In addition there were two (normal) reflections, one on the left and one on the right. I took a chair and sat in front of the mirror for more than an hour.

And then a strange thought came into my head. Do the four people – myself and the three reflections – also exist when I take away the mirror?

I am a person with a real existence and with two eyes, which, from a stereochemical point of view I would describe as two asymmetrical centres. I have spent long enough studying spatially constructed chemical compounds with two asymmetrical chemical centres – the idea is fixed in my brain like a mark branded onto a calf.

All four 'persons' are equidistant from the centre of the mirror. When I reach my hand towards this central point (all points along the vertical axis of the mirrors are central points), the three reflected hands reach out towards me. One feature of the space in front of my hand is that I cannot enter it, because all four hands approach each other at the same time. As soon as you touch the mirror, the illusion disappears.

From the centre of the mirror, space is broken up at right-angles into four quadrants. Because infinite space exists around every point, this space has a strange angular dimensional geometry of true intersecting planes. These intersecting planes are visibly demonstrated by Plato's mirror. This space mirror effectively makes it possible to see a hidden phenomenon, such as a mental picture, an idea.

I have always wondered about the dimensions of infinite

space around a point. It cannot be three-dimensional with regard to length, breadth and height. I was now sitting in front of a space mirror and could see the solution in front of my own eyes: two intersecting planes. Each of these planes is quadriform and measurable in square units such as square centimetres (cm^2).

When I multiply these two intersecting planes with each other, I am actually squaring something that is already squared, and the resultant units are to the power 4 (cm^4). From two dimensions we now have four.

Such a space has a special geometrical feature. A three-dimensional body – for instance, a cube – has three axes at right-angles to each other. This is therefore referred to as x-y-z axial geometry.

The four-dimensional infinite space around a point (in this case every point of intersection of the mirror) does not possess a z axis but only x^2 y^2 plane geometry.

This notion of 'four dimensions' has nothing to do with the popular combination in physics of the three dimensions of space with one dimension of time.

I was still sitting in front of my mirror when I suddenly clenched my fist and watched my reflections do the same. If physicists had been using an inappropriate geometry to present a physical calculation of space around the atomic nucleus, I was now apparently about to become a theoretical physicist. If infinite, empty space always has a quadruple structure because the world is always 'two-dimensional squared' at every point, the four quantum numbers of the electrons must in fact be a geometrical necessity, whereas so far this has only been empirical knowledge, derived from experience.

But if I could finally discover why electrons happened to have four quantum numbers, I would also find out why atoms have no more than three components. It would then be clear why there are only three stable nuclear particles and why all additional particles that are believed to have been found are in fact not really components of the atom at all but merely events resulting from energy-tracings and photographic recordings. It was possible that a hitherto unknown law of pure number theory could be hidden behind this triple nature of the atomic nucleus, whereas the quadruple nature of the third particle, the electron, would have a purely spatial explanation.

I immediately hit on an incredible connection. My training in nuclear chemistry and biochemistry was now at last bearing real fruit.

The atomic structure makes use of the numbers 3 and 4, and these are also the numbers used by our genetic material. Our cells contain cell nuclei, which in turn consist of chromosomes. Examination of these chromosomes has shown that they consist of giant chains of molecules which because of their complicated name (deoxyribonucleic acid) are known by the abbreviation DNA.

DNA consists entirely of only three chemical components: **phosphoric acid (P)**, a **sugar (S)**, and a **base (B)**. This mysterious substance consists of chains of phosphoric acid and sugar molecules in the following arrangement:

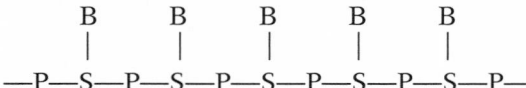

A base is attached to each sugar molecule. This comprises any one of four different bases – and nobody knows why there should have to be precisely four – **thiamine**, **adenine**, **cytosine**, **guanine**.

What would happen if the same law were to be found behind the components of atoms (3) and the quantum numbers of electrons (4) as exists behind the components of DNA (3) and the base pairings (4)? This would then for the first time give us information on why pure isotopes – which occur in atomic nuclei, and amino acids, which occur in DNA – obey the same fundamental laws, namely 1 + 19.

I walked away from my space mirror deep in thought. In a few months I would be 40 years old. In two months the pharmacy, which was to give me financial independence to pursue these matters further, would finally be ready. My thoughts in front of the mirror had been primarily in the area of theoretical physics. It seemed that Professor Hauser with his ten-year prediction had been right after all.

In former decades there used to be a lot of discussion concerning the nature of space, a notion that clearly contains a paradox. Any line drawn on paper is one-dimensional. The medium surrounding it, however, has to have one dimension more. This is obviously true in that a piece of paper is a surface and thus two-dimensional. Consequently, the medium in which the piece of paper is located must be three-dimensional. This is true in the case of the room in which the piece of paper is located. However, logic requires that a three-dimensional object must be surrounded by a four-dimensional space. Because this space can not be visualized, mathematicians at the end of the 19th century finally ended the discussion and introduced the idea of any number of dimensions. The notion of 'any number' always leads to the question 'also an infinite number?', and the answer was given that an infinite number of dimensions was perfectly permissible. Mathematics is a human invention and the mathematical mind wanted to free itself from the third and impalpable fourth dimension.

Although I had discovered a totally new geometry – four-dimensional infinite space around every point of finite size, and thus, of course, around every three-dimensional body – I could not expect that my ideas would for a moment be entertained by any mathematician. In this world nothing can, or can be allowed to, be wrong which for hundreds of years has been blessed by scientific approval.

Multi-dimensional space has nothing to do with reality. For that very reason physicists did not take up the idea – because they could not afford to ignore reality. Instead, they created their own fourth dimension (space-time). But space-time is also totally unconnected with reality. To complete the confusion, people have been speaking for the last hundred years about whether space (the universe) is curved. Scientists still have not been able to decide whether it is concave or convex. Because the curvature of space has always appeared to me to be nothing more than a mental aberration, the idea of any fruitful discussions with physicists has also proved to be an illusion so far.

The matter did have one advantage, however. I would be forced to come to grips with deeper problems of mathematics if I were to make progress. Whoever wants really to get to the bottom of a science has to occupy himself with its history. This fact is unfortunately for the most part ignored today. This is one reason we currently train specialists who totally lack an overall picture of their own field. By investigating the history of

111

mathematics and the eras in which Leibniz, Euler and Gauss lived and worked, and in which they made radical progress, I finally discovered my love for mathematics and for the science which Gauss described as his 'queen' of all science – number theory.

CHAPTER TEN

CONCERNING ELECTRONS AND PRIME NUMBER TWINS

At the beginning of any study of number theory there is a list of the numerical series in which the prime numbers are identified: we show them here in bold type.

1, **2**, **3**, 4, **5**, 6, **7**, 8, 9, 10, **11**, 12, **13**, 14, 15, 16, **17**, 18, **19**, 20, 21, 22, **23**, 24, 25, 26, 27, 28, **29**, 30, **31**, 32, 33, 34, 35, 36, **37**, 38, 39, 40, **41**, 42, **43**, 44, 45, 46, **47**, 48, 49, ...

Each of the first three numbers is only divisible by itself or by the number one and all three are prime numbers. Because the root of the number 1 can be easily calculated ($-1 \times -1 = +1$), it is by definition not considered to be a prime number. The usual sequence of prime numbers is therefore

$$2, 3, 5, 7, 11, 13, ...$$

No doubts have ever been raised about this definition, and mathematicians have therefore fallen headlong into a trap of enormous proportions.

A man from classical times would believe that the gods on Olympus had devised a grand trick to play on us, as if they were forced to grant us mathematics as a tool, but to compensate for this permission they blinded us before releasing us into the world. Homeric laughter would echo in the ears of a Greek mathematician when he grasped that the gods had from the very beginning programmed our human arrogance by closing our eyes to the unit that is at the foundation of all numbers, the number 1.

After 1 was removed from the sequence of prime numbers, the first prime number was the number 2. Among the infinite number of prime numbers, it is the only one that is even. The fact that this was simply accepted was the second major source of error, and led inevitably with the next prime number, 3, to a trap in which we lost sight of the divine order contained in the numbers 1, 2 and 3.

I was now 40 years old and was working in a soundproof room furnished only with a bed, desk and chair, just as I had done as a student. I also had the three necessary tools: paper, pencil and pocket calculator. I had the volume of numbers displayed in front of me and considered the numbers 1, 2 and 3. I had found a triplicate in all disciplines. In the myths and legends of all cultures, the numbers 1, 2 and 3 played a very prominent part (eg three guesses, three wishes). Was it not ironic that mathematics, the subject that deals with numbers, should happen to be the one field in which the numbers 1, 2 and 3 have no special significance?

I had wanted to find out what secrets were hidden in silicon hydride. Although I had anticipated the explosion in the laboratory, I had accepted the risk. I now wanted to find out something else, and again I saw an immense danger approaching. Myths and legends are full of stories of people having to choose between three paths, or doors. Like the hero in the story I now had to find the correct door to escape my destruction. I had studied for 20 years and had devoted the next 10 years of my life to my quest to discover the riddle of the universe. If I had not achieved this goal by the time I was 50, I was resolved to cease all my study in science. It would be equivalent to admitting total defeat. All predictions of the future would then be shown to be illusory.

I knew that the first three numbers would contain a very explosive mixture.

What does a bomb disposal expert do when some inner voice tells him that an electronic booby-trap is contained in the fuse of a bomb? The answer is that he keeps well away from the fuse!

And so I started my examination of the prime numbers with the prime number 5:

5, 6, **7**, 8, 9, 10, **11**, 12, **13**, 14, 15, 16, **17**, 18, **19**, 20, 21, 22, **23**, 24, 25, 26, 27, 28, **29**, 30, **31**, 32, 33, 34, 35, 36, **37**, 38, 39, 40, **41**, 42, **43**, 44, 45, 46, **47**, 48, 49, ...

When I studied this arrangement I discerned a system that was related to multiples of the number 6. Around the number 6, the prime number twins 5 and 7 are found; around the number 12 there are the twins 11 and 13; and around 18 the twins 17 and 19. When we move on a further six places, we should expect to find the twins 23 and 25. However, here the natural sequence of the three first prime number twins is not continued: 25 is not a prime number, it is the square of the original prime number 5. Consequently, the number twins 23 and 25 begin a new section which continues to recur to infinity. Prime numbers or prime number twins will always occur around a number divisible by 6, although these positions – around a multiple of 6 – will for combinational reasons be occupied by products of the previous prime numbers –

$$5, 7, 11, 13, 17, 19, ...$$

– 25 as product of 5 × 5, 35 as the product of 5 × 7, 49 as the product of 7 × 7, 55 as the product of 5 × 11, etc.

This pattern based on 6 means that the product 0 × 6 = 0 must be found at six to the left of the number 6. The number 0 must therefore also be surrounded by a number twin:

$$-1, 0, 1$$

The sequence of the first four number twins is therefore

$$(-1;1) — \boxed{(5;7) — (11;13) — (17;19)}$$

Such a coding exemplified by 1 and 3 had been my quest for half a lifetime.

Because electron twins are arranged in circular 'orbits' in the atomic shells, I now left the linear mode of presenting the natural numbers and noted them in a clockwise direction. Between the prime numbers, either one or three numbers are alternately indicated. I therefore had to note three more non-prime numbers after 19.

What I discovered here resembled a clock with a 24-hour

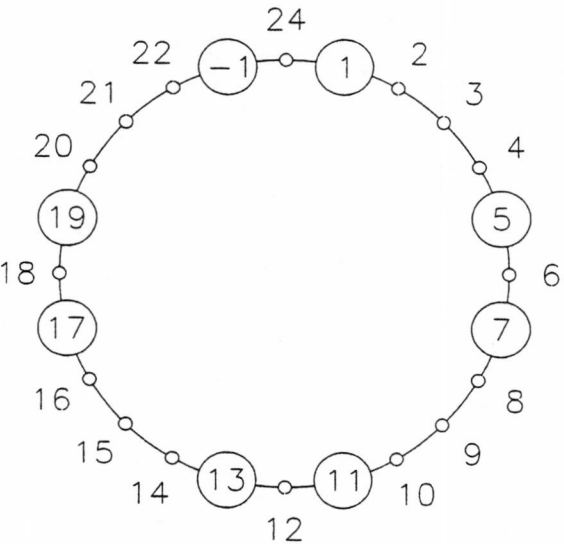

Figure 1

division of time. The double 12-hour clock was invented in ancient Egypt – curiously in the place where, for the first time in history, humans calculated using the decimal system. The ancient Egyptian hieroglyphic alphabet consisted of 24 letters (it is a consonantal alphabet). Because the number of signs was greatly expanded by the addition of signs for syllables and words, it is difficult to find an Egyptologist today who is aware that every work in ancient Egyptian can be written with these 24 letters. Unfortunately, no papyrus texts written by a priest of ancient Egypt has survived, for they guarded their knowledge very carefully, particularly the correlation between the numbers 24 and 6, which they considered to be sacred. The story of Creation in six days has its origin in this notion.

When I considered this circular arrangement of numbers deriving from the number 1, I obtained a ring deriving from the number 1 and seven prime numbers. Clearly the position which now contained the number -1 also contained the number 23. This ring is a curious phenomenon. It consists of the number pairs -1, +1 and three further prime number twins. The comparison with the inert gas shell consisting of one s-electron pair and three p-electron twins is astonishing. The number 24 is also found at point zero; 25 must therefore be located at a superimposed level above the 1, 26 above the 2, etc. The prime number 25 is above the prime number 5.

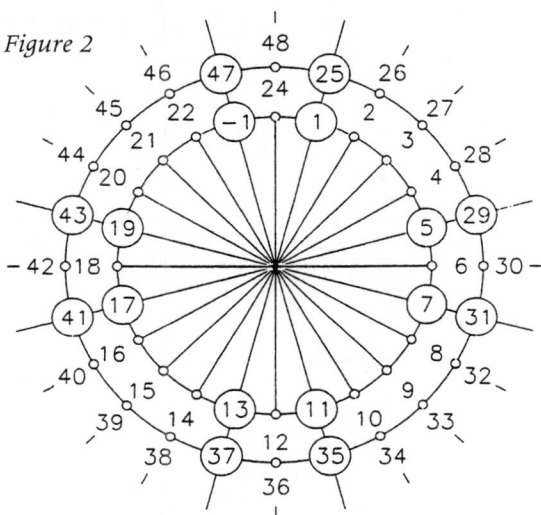

Figure 2

I prepared a drawing in which I joined all numbers on the first circle to the centre. The result had – even visually – an astonishing similarity with the atomic model: a minute nucleus of conspicuously small size in relation to the giant surrounding electron shells.

All prime numbers up to the number 48 were located on eight rays. But what about the numbers on the remaining sixteen rays? Sixteen numbers, exactly half of the remaining 32 numbers were divisible by 3 and the other sixteen were multiples of 2. Was it possible that these multiples of 2 and 3 were derived from the basic numbers 2 and 3, just as the prime numbers derive from the number ± 1? The numbers 1, 2 and 3 as initial elements of the three number categories of equal size would therefore for logical reasons also have to be prime numbers:

$$1 \rightarrow 5, 7, 11, 13, 17, 19, 23, 25, 29, 31, \ldots$$
$$2 \rightarrow 4, 8, 10, 14, 16, 20, 22, 26, 28, 32, \ldots$$
$$3 \rightarrow 6, 9, 12, 15, 18, 21, 24, 27, 30, 33, \ldots$$

And that is what they are in the original sense of the word! The expression 'prime number' comes as a translation from the French (*nombre primeur*) meaning 'first number'.

These three basic rows can be better illustrated in three separate cyclical sketches than in a simple linear arrangement. It turned out to be a correct decision to have omitted the

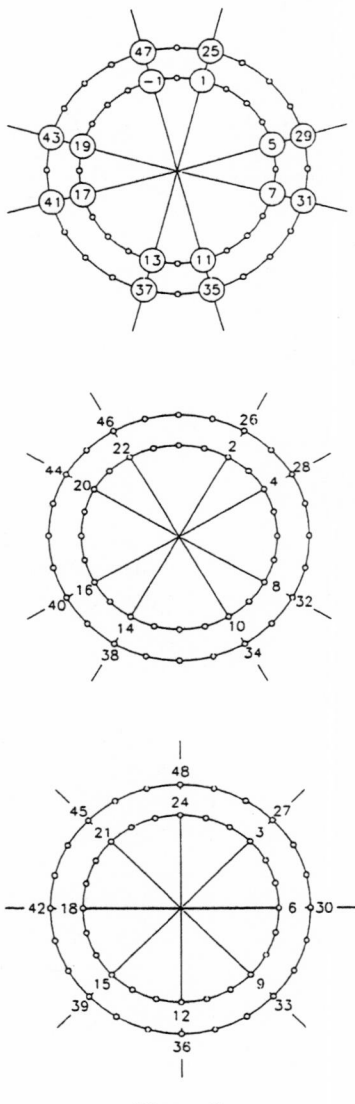

Figure 3

numbers 1, 2 and 3 for the time being. Only by doing so could I develop the unusual concept that the numbers are of three types, even when this idea overturned centuries of dogma concerning prime numbers.

I now had evidence of why all countable matter has the same triple nature which had served me all my life as a faithful signpost.

The recurrence of the number 6 in the prime numbers that I had found had already occurred to another person well before my time. As might have been expected, this was Leibniz.

He perceived that prime numbers larger than 3 always surround multiples of the number 6 with the addition of 1 or 5 ($6n+1$ or $6n+5$ for $n = 1, 2, 3, ...$). He did not manage, however, to reach the correct formula $6n \pm 1$ for $n = 0, 1, 2, 3, 4, ...$

It is true that the importance of the number 0 was only just beginning to be realized at that time, for the Baroque period witnessed an intensive study of mathematical theory. But everything smaller than zero (like the number -1) was beyond the bounds of standard logic. (The number 0 as a place-filler in larger numbers and the number -1 in accountancy were, of course, known at the time.) Leibniz was thus unable to recognize the triple basis of numbers.

The sum of the numbers 1, 2 and 3 ($1 + 2 + 3$) and the product of the numbers 1, 2 and 3 ($1 \times 2 \times 3$) also give the value 6. That both the sum and the product of three numbers have the same value does not occur anywhere else in the infinite set of numbers. The number 6 is therefore the scaffold on which the prime numbers within the natural numbers are built. The reasons for the existence of the prime numbers, whose distribution appears arbitrary when they are observed in the conventional way, is solely and exclusively a result of the structure of the number ± 1 and the number 0. The significance of the distribution of prime numbers simply cannot be seen from a linear presentation of the numbers.

With my first cyclical presentation of the numbers (figures 1 and 2) I had to account for how the number 24 can occur in the same place as the number 0. But the position occupied by the number 0 also happened to be occupied by the number 23.

I managed to solve this problem by inserting a 0 shell below the first circle of numbers.

This decisive step was all the easier for me after I had recognized the connection between my circle of numbers and the atomic model, and because I was aware of the expression 'inner shell' from the latter. Every atom of every element can take at most only two electrons on its innermost orbit. On the next shell there is a maximum of eight electrons. In the case of inert gases, only eight electrons can occur in the outermost shell.

The number −1 did not have a partner on the right-hand side because its logical partner, the number +1, introduces the series of the whole numbers on the shell above (figure 4).

The drawing now shows four double rays on which prime numbers can occur. It was based on a geometrical form that I had seen so often on my brother's uniform when he worked for St John Ambulance in his youth. This cross of the order of Christian knights is still today on almost all medals awarded to people for special achievements!

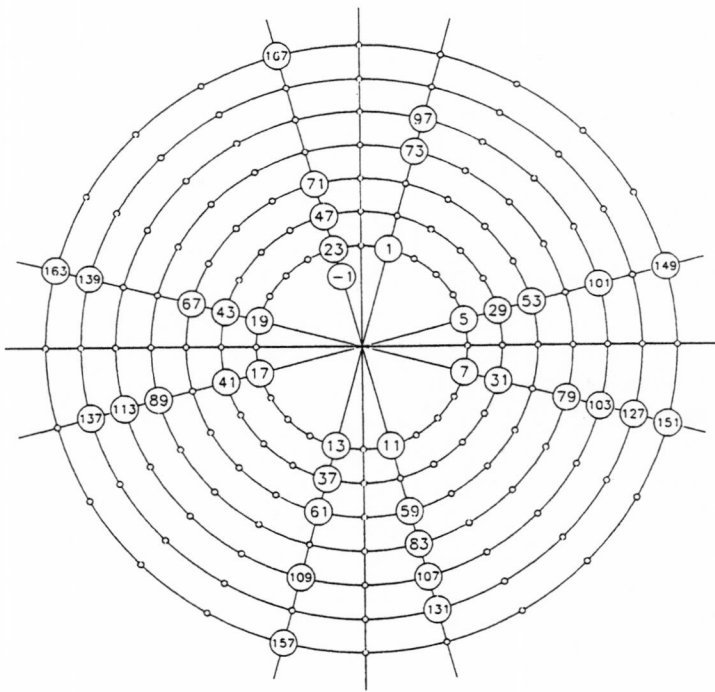

Figure 4

I therefore decided to name this order of prime numbers 'The Prime Number Cross' because of the cross structure. The shell of an inert gas contains eight electrons and this Prime Number Cross contains eight rays. The cross structure of the two axes intersecting at right-angles allows the two-dimensional Prime Number Cross to be rotated in the mind – both around a horizontal and a vertical axis (the quadrate of each axis produces a surface, and these surfaces must therefore intersect).

The shells (number circles) expand around the central point towards infinity. This is the infinite numeric space around a point of finite size.

If the Prime Number Cross has the dimension of a surface, two intersecting numeric crosses must therefore have the dimension of a square of a square, and must be four-dimensional. A 'squared square' area in this sense can not be easily conjured up in our imagination. It can, however, be demonstrated by outstretched fingers threaded at a right-angle through each other – the gesture they make when some people want to pray. These surfaces intersect each other. The four-dimensional nature of the shell space only applies for an infinite number of shells. The infinite space around a point would become a three-dimensional body, a sphere, if infinity were itself to become a limit.

The experience with the space mirror in my pharmacy stayed on my mind for one whole year. But only when I recognized the infinite space around a point as numeric space did the full weight of my discovery occur to me. The expansion of a light wave emerging from a point flows as a spherical wave to infinity. And because the speed of light is finite, the expansion of the wave is linked to time. No physicist of today denies the real existence of space and time. But what mysterious medium controls the structure of the wave? It is a well-known fact that the spherical wave must consist of two segments standing in vertical relation to each other. The reason for it, however, cannot be explained because x^2y^2 geometry is as yet unexplored.

When infinity and its triple nature are one, the continuum of space and time in the conventional physical sense cannot exist. Numbers are the third component of infinity. Only the concealed triplicate of

space
time
numbers

can lead us out of the cul-de-sac of our picture of the world that is trapped in finite concepts. One absolute consequence of this is that numbers must now be granted a real existence.

Numbers can, of course, not be seen. But space and time can also not be seen. Infinite space and infinite time cannot be registered by our finite faculties of imagination. The infinite numbers, however, by virtue of their prime number structure contain not only a numeric aesthetic, but are also the key to the material world and a medium of information to infinity. Only they can provide the background for the natural constants, for beyond the realms of proof infinity necessarily exists by its own right in that 'nothing' can not exist.

And there it was again – the puzzle of my youth. Why does the speed of light have to have the value that we can now measure to so many places after the decimal point? Does this have anything to do with the numeric structure of space?

I became increasingly isolated in my room and searched for some idea that could be of further help to me. Why do the atoms of all elements consist of three atomic particles – proton, neutron and electron? Why do the electrons contain four quantum numbers? Why should precisely 81 stable elements exist, no more and no less?

The number 81 is the product of $3 \times 3 \times 3 \times 3$; $3^4 = 81$. The numbers 3, 4 and 81 had been on my mind for years, and suddenly their interrelation appeared as a '**3-to-the-power-of-4 law**'.

If God had simply arranged the 81 elements according to the ordinal numbers 1, 2, 3, ... 81, researchers would have discovered this fact a long time ago. They would have come to grips with the problem. Instead of this, the list of stable elements has bismuth, with an atomic number of 83, as the highest element. It was not considered important that two of the elements on the list can only be artificially synthesized.

I have always been interested in the inversion of numbers up to 100 – or, to phrase that better, I have been interested in the special features of these periodic fractions. I remembered that

the reciprocal value of 81 had particularly aroused my interest:
$1/81 = 0.01234567901234567901... = 0.012345679$ .... The
numbers 012345679 recurred, with the number 8 always
missing. The fraction $1/81$ can also be presented in an even more
unusual way:[1]

$$1/81 = 0.0123456789(10)(11)(12)(13)...$$

It is not particularly easy to comprehend this mode of
presentation but the effort made will be rewarded by a most
satisfactory effect.

Because no numbers exist in the decimal system greater than
9, the numbers 10, 11, 12 etc. are placed in brackets. The
number (10) in the familiar decimal form increases the prior 9
to 10, and this in turn increases the prior 8 by 1 to 9. In the
recurring fraction 0.012345679 ... the number 8 is missing. This
prevents the reciprocal value of 81 being visually linked to all
numerical series. This idea appeared wonderful to my eyes
because now the number 81 appears as a reciprocal value for
the atomic numbers of the elements. The missing 8 is an illusion
which had until then blocked my way to the novel notion that
the reciprocal value of the order of all numbers 00123456789 ...
is the number 81.

I have deliberately omitted the decimal point in front of the
first 0 because it serves only to indicate the decimal fraction
which is to be read from the left to the right.

It is clear that the 81 elements and their atomic numbers 0, 1,
2, 3, 4, 5 ... are reciprocally linked to each other (the atomic
number 0 is assigned to the neutron). Nature must itself
therefore be arranged according to the decimal system. This
seemed to be plausible because numerical space around a point
requires such a regularity for its expansion. The material that
occurs in space and was certainly not generated magically there
only fits there if it is constructed according to those regular laws
in which the space is arranged, just as a key only fits into a
special lock.

Because we humans only have ten fingers, we calculate using
the decimal system. This would not have been so summarily
consigned to the realm of chance by our mathematicians if they
had also been familiar with chemistry, because they would then
have known that the stable chemical elements are all

categorized in ten types of isotopes.

If the number 1 is divided by 81, it is well known that the 81 must first be expanded to 100. Even when the same calculation is done in some system other than the decimal system, the division cannot be calculated without combination with the number 0.

$$100/81 = 1 + \text{remainder } 19$$

I had been studying the two numbers 1 and 19 for 20 years because of the 20 amino acids and 20 pure isotopes without making any perceptible progress. Perhaps finally I had now taken up the scent.

The residual value 19 must again be divided by 81:

$$19/81 = 0.234567 \ldots$$

The prime number 19 is responsible for the ensuing chronological numeric series of the decimal system (without the 1).

The result of the calculation $100 \div 81$ is $1 + \text{remainder } 19$.

I had finally got behind the secret of the numbers 19 and 81. I was not going to let go now. Suddenly I felt a flash of lightning pass through me. My gaze turned to the calendar on the wall. It was marked with the year 1981.

NOTE
1 The proof for this presentation of 1/81 is simple:
$$1/81 = 1/9 \times 1/9 = 0.1111 \ldots \times 0.1111 \ldots$$
$$= 0.0 \, (1) \times (1 + 1) \times (1 + 1 + 1) \times (1 + 1 + 1 + 1) \ldots$$
[Cauchy-product as formulated by the French mathematician A. L. Cauchy]

$$
\begin{array}{r}
0.1111 \ldots \times 0.1111 \ldots \\
\hline
0 \\
01111 \ldots \\
01111 \ldots \\
01111 \ldots \\
\cdot \\
\cdot \\
\cdot \\
\hline
0.0123 \ldots \\
= 0.0123456789(10)(11)(12) \ldots
\end{array}
$$

CHAPTER ELEVEN

PUTTING BOUNDS ON THE INFINITE

I was exhausted by the long months of intensive meditation. This was but a taste of what was to come for me over the next years. But despite torturing loneliness and physical collapse, I was euphoric because I knew I was making progress. Often the only light in my life would be when my young daughter burst into my room and shouted the direct order: 'Daddy, stop thinking!' In such moments I could drop everything immediately.

Purely abstract mathematical thought was being repeatedly replaced in my mind by intensive study of the history of the world and the history of mathematics, natural science and philosophy. The history of modern science that finally led to the construction of the atomic bomb was written here in Europe. And here in Europe, the spiritual idea was also born which would overcome this nuclear nightmare. It will not be possible to simply dismantle the bombs. This assertion is made only by confused (or confusing) politicians, because it is impossible to dismantle the knowledge of how to construct the bomb. Such knowledge is even being developed further. The million-fold increase in explosive power and its possible deployment at any point of the globe within minutes is not even kept a secret from the world's population. It is also well known that fear itself prevents people from recognizing the full extent of the danger.

Though the fission that occurs in a uranium or plutonium

bomb, which in turn can be used to ignite a hydrogen bomb, a tiny amount of matter is transformed into electromagnetic energy (light and heat). This happens according to Einstein's famous formula containing the speed of light. But we know nothing about the real essence of this natural constant. Einstein always referred to the speed of light with a rounded-up value:

$$3 \times 10^{10} \times \frac{cm}{s}$$

It is probable that neither he nor other physicists even toyed with the idea that the absolute value of the speed of light, which they calculated at 2.9979, could in fact be the number 3, or, more correctly, three times the number 10^{10} – although the absolute length and time measurements are of secondary importance because they appear in the calculation as a length/time relationship.

I had always been fascinated by the beautiful roundness of the number 3 that Einstein always used, but I had not till now been bold enough to suspect that the number 3 coupled with a power of 10 could itself be the absolute value and not merely a rounded-up value for the speed of light. By this time, however, I felt courageous enough to put the boot into this dogma. The oft-repeated objection that the decimal system and the measurement of length called the centimetre and the measurement of time called the second are all of them actually arbitrary or coincidental (because they are replaceable) has itself become a dogma.[1]

Dogmas are judgements that have achieved the status of religious beliefs through long general acceptance and by definition therefore tend to have a long life. In reality dogmas are collective prejudices. Rupert Lay expressed it even more drastically: 'Dogma, and invoking dogma, is a classical sign of stupidity.'

If numbers exist, and if the decimal system is also not a coincidence, then – I reasoned – the measurements of length, weight and time (centimetre-gram-second, the system) could be identical with the absolute dimensions in which nature is arranged. With regard to the dimension of time, this immediately appeared plausible to me because the Babylonians set the length of a second as the 3,600th part of an hour. Such a value may come as a bit of a surprise. It is, however, the product of the squares of the Pythagorean numbers 3, 4 and 5.

$$3,600 = 3^2 \times 4^2 \times 5^2$$

An hour was defined during the Babylonian period as the 24th part of a day (one rotation of the Earth). This number was very carefully chosen: 24 is the product of $1 \times 2 \times 3 \times 4$ and is the foundation of the natural prime number rhythm, which the Babylonians undoubtedly knew about.

That physics was paralysed in dogma became more and more clear to me. The factor 3 within the equation for the speed of light is not recognized immediately because, in a world that sees its origin in the chance events of the Big Bang, the mere coincidence of the measured values may under no circumstances be put at risk.

The exact value for the speed of light as $3 \times 10^{10} = 30,000,000,000$ can no longer be put down to mere chance. However, because each mistake brings further mistakes with it, any person blinded by such self-imposed blinkers might also miss the fact that the number 3 also plays a decisive part in other natural constants of physics. All natural constants in fact consist of the three units

number (eg 2.9979 ...)
factor (eg 10^{10})
dimension (eg centimetres per second)

After all, nobody looks for something they do not want to find. But it is impossible to make progress in physics if new and unconventional questions are not considered at some stage.

The speed of light in which the number 3 and the triplicate appear occurs in Einstein's equation in connection with two other dimensions, so that a second triplicate appears. I shall explain these in individual steps so that the extent of the elegance of the equation can be fully appreciated.

Einstein's formula is mostly quoted in the 'abbreviated' version

$$E = mc^2$$

But it should actually be written

$$E^2 = m^2c^4$$

The constant corresponding to the speed of light appears with the exponent 4. If the value of $c = 3 \times 10^{10}\ \frac{cm}{s}$ is inserted in the unabbreviated equation, the by now familiar expression $3^4 = 81$ appears. This gives the following equation for the energy-mass relationship:

$$\frac{E^2}{m^2} = 81 \times 10^{40}\ \frac{cm^4}{s^4}$$

Because the number 81 contains the extraordinarily interesting reciprocal value 0.0123456789(10)(11)(12)..., we can represent the equation reciprocally:

$$\frac{m^2}{E^2} = 0.01234... \times 10^{-40}\ \frac{s^4}{cm^4}$$

On considering the equation and its reciprocal equation, I was suddenly filled with a feeling of awe. For in both these equations the term cm^4 appears. From this perspective space acquires a four-dimensional structure. For a long time I had had an idea of how a space with the dimension 'length to the power 4' would appear. It would have to be two vertically intersecting surfaces which would divide space into four infinite segments with no external limit.

I had got the idea that there are only 81 stable elements from the fact that there are three components of all atoms. I now postulated that matter only fits into such space as is arranged according to the same principles as the matter itself. Because I now took the absolute numerical factor 3 as the speed of light, the number 81 had to appear in Einstein's formula as a quantity, and reciprocally as an infinite decimal number of the order of the whole numbers. Einstein's equation now displays its actual mathematical significance. Something is either material and countable, or it disappears and dissolves. It then spreads out into infinity as a wave phenomenon, just as a number is a realization of a quantity and its reciprocal value is a diminution towards eternity.

My interpretation of Einstein's formula would, however, not be taken seriously in the scientific world until I had proof that the speed of light was linked to the number 3.

In 1984, however, I discovered the rigorous mathematical proof that numerical space (prime number space) contains a numerical expansion constant with the factor 3. This led in 1986 to a breakthrough in the question: 'Was matter (in the form of protons and electrons) created or does it exist by virtue of the nature of infinity?'

As I pondered on the fact that substance is in fact inextricably linked to the space that holds the substance, and the effect of energy is similarly connected to time, I suddenly saw Einstein's formula in the form I had expressed it (the factor 10^{40} is omitted for the sake of clarity; ~ = proportional).

$$\frac{E^2}{m^2} \sim 81 \times \frac{cm^4}{s^4}$$

I suddenly fixed on two separate elements in this equation which have a famous physical connection to each other: the square of energy $[E^2]$ and the second to the power 4 $[s^4]$. It is difficult at first to conceptualize anything that might be described in the expression s^4. The term 'space-time' is, however, familiar to everybody. A finite space is three-dimensional (to the power 3) and an infinite space four-dimensional (to the power 4). With regard to the time in which an electromagnetic wave expands through space, there is a four-dimensional factor which can be expressed as time squared to the power 2.

The energy of an electromagnetic wave is related to the number of oscillations per second. One oscillation per second is described as 1 hertz in physics. The relationship that emerges involves a connection showing energy and reciprocal time as pure four-dimensional inversion.

In the same way, matter and reciprocal space can be presented as a four-dimensional phenomenon (m^2 = mass squared and cm^4 = area squared).

We can therefore now separate two partial equations from Einstein's equation (~ = proportional).

$$E^2 \sim \frac{1}{time\ squared^2} \quad \text{and} \quad m^2 \sim \frac{1}{area^2}$$

The reversal of an infinite four-dimensional space produces, according to this formula, an expression for matter which is physically linked to mass. The infinity of space will then exist reciprocally as points of matter. This meant that I had an explanation for the existence of electrons and protons at last. They had to exist because four-dimensional space, in contrast to three-dimensional space, requires by its very nature central points of finite size. These points would then also have to be fitted with a potentially infinite 'magic' from which our whole material world evolved. When I think of electrons and protons and how they can work 'magic' with their electrical charges, it is not such a strange notion that these particles did not emerge from some other particles at some time in the past but instead exist because of the nature of infinity.

All that is now missing is the third familiar part of the formula, the quantity 81, which reciprocally represents our number order.

$$81 = \frac{1}{0.01234\ldots}$$

This means that Einstein's equation not only connects the three most important physical dimensions which we can perceive with our senses (matter, energy and quantity), but also the reverse of these dimensions (space, time and numerical sequence). These inversions are linked to infinity and are accessible to us through our ability to conceptualize. The interface between the finity of observation and the infinite realm of the imagination is the human mind.

I matter and space
II energy and time
III quantity and numerical sequence

are linked together through this one equation.

I formulated the corollary thus: 'If matter did not exist, not one single atom, there would also be no space.' But if only the two of them can exist at the same time, then the one would have to be the other, only reversed. Where there is no movement, there is also no time. Energy can therefore be nothing else than the reverse of time. The only way to connect space and time is to bring them down to their reciprocal dimensions, matter and energy. In order that no nonsense emerges in this procedure, there must be a plan, and this must be the only one that exists – the numbers 0, 1, 2, 3, 4 ... as ordered by the Prime Number Cross.

Behind this in turn we find the first eight primary numbers: 1, 5, 7, 11, 13, 17, 19, 23 as the initial elements of the eight prime number rays.

This entirely novel notion of structural infinity around a point can only be established and clarified by the geometry of the twin prime numbers. This allows our world to be registered for the first time: material substance as the means of putting bounds to infinity.

In our contemporary physical picture, it is simply accepted that matter is energy in bundles. Because the term 'energy' refers to electromagnetic energy and this is not capable of standing still – it has no choice other than to expand at the speed of light – the notion can be seen as patently absurd.

In 1982 I made very little progress. Every pathway seemed to be blocked. I was totally at my wit's end. And in the process of my continuous deep meditation and research, in which I once more delved into all the branches of science just in case I had overlooked something important, I again returned to the building-blocks of life.

Nature is again made up of precisely three basic components: **phosphoric acid, sugars** and **bases**. One part of this threesome – the base – consists in turn of four different chemical compounds.

The four bases determine 20 amino acids. When the 'genetic code' was deciphered back in the 1960s, it was discovered that an amino acid is always determined by three successive bases. At that time the artificial expression 'base triplet' was introduced, but the importance of the number three was again neglected. The main argument at the time was the sentence that began with the little word 'If'.

'If a code-word consists of two signs, there would be $4^2 = 16$ possibilities.' But this would be too few for 20 amino acids. And for this reason, it was inferred, nature had to work with three signs in order to reach the larger number. Because $4^3 = 64$, this combinational calculation coincidentally provided quite a few possibilities more than were needed.

I was forced to return to the question of why nature had to use precisely 20 amino acids for the production of protein. There

131

had to be some connection with chemical elements and with isotopes.

Of all elements in the periodic system, the first element – hydrogen, which has the atomic number 1 – is the maverick of the herd and was for that reason the subject of considerable dispute among chemists for decades. In the Periodic Table it is generally listed among the alkaline metals, because like these it has only one electron and reacts positively as a monovalent. Hydrogen is, however, quite the opposite of a metal – it is a non-metal, and clever chemists have therefore attempted to include the element in the seventh group of the Periodic Table among the halogens. Hydrogen does in fact occur in chemistry with the value −1 and links up with metals to form metal hydrides. The Periodic Table was therefore created for all elements, not just for the first element.

Hydrogen is the basic building-block of matter. Just as all numbers can in the end be derived from the number 1, all elements on the Earth were created in a flash in an exploding star from the first element, hydrogen.

Without hydrogen the periodic system would contain only 80 stable elements. Of these, precisely 20 elements are pure isotopes, having that arrangement which had occupied me for so long: 1 + 19.

Not the number 4 but the number 3 must be made the basis of all enquiry geared towards finding out why precisely 20 amino acids are necessary for life.

However, this can only be explained properly with a 3^4 law. According to reasoning similar to the case of the elements, from 80 stereochemical possibilities exactly a quarter were selected, and probably for the same reason they came in the sequence 1 and 19.

This idea finally allowed me to go further. It made me go and fetch an old chemistry book that had been lying for a long time in a box in our cellar.

In the textbook I found a table of elements and examined them with special reference to the frequency of their isotopes. I stared at this table for a long time and saw how conspicuously the elements with only one mass-number – ie the pure isotopes – are distinguished from the other elements. Just as the observer of a three-dimensional drawing after he has donned his 3-D glasses requires a moment for space and depth to register in his mind, I gradually realized that a second group of elements was also conspicuous. I saw that, like the pure isotopes, all had uneven atomic numbers but two mass numbers. I began to understand: when I counted them there would be 19 elements just as with the pure isotopes. And in fact there were exactly 19 elements, all with uneven atomic numbers and all with double isotopes.

I was speechless with amazement and wondered: 'Why has nobody noticed this before?' I had noticed it because I had subtracted from the 83 elements the two non-existing elements with atomic numbers 43 and 61 and hydrogen, with atomic number 1. I was thus left with 80 elements, a number that is divisible by 4.

There are now exactly 19 double isotopes because one element, potassium, which has the atomic number 19 is the only element that does not obey the following rule: **all stable elements with uneven atomic numbers are either pure or double isotopes.**

Potassium has the atomic number 19 and as an alkaline metal is completely normal from a chemical point of view. Yet in nuclear chemistry it has a very special characteristic: despite its uneven atomic number it is neither a pure nor a double isotope but rather a multiple isotope with a total of three isotopes.

The even-numbered element 4, beryllium, is a pure isotope and leads the sequence of the total of 20 pure isotopes.

In the case of double isotopes, the element with the lowest atomic number is an even number. This is element number 2 (helium). It is a double isotope despite its even atomic number. I spontaneously set this element above the other 19 double isotopes. My heart was beating wildly and I could have cried for joy.

How often had I been thinking about the 1 and 19 pure isotopes! Why had it not occurred to me earlier to examine the remaining uneven numbers for their numbers of isotopes? I had now found a second group of elements, the 1 and 19 double isotopes.

The discovery of the mysterious sequence 1 + 19 of the uneven pure isotopes and the uneven 1 + 19 double isotopes suddenly presented me with the opportunity of also dividing the

	Pure isotopes	Double isotopes

Table 2. Elements with uneven atomic numbers

	Pure isotopes	Double isotopes
1	$_4$Be	$_2$He
2	$_9$F	$_3$Li
3	$_{11}$Na	$_5$B
4	$_{13}$Al	$_7$N
5	$_{15}$P	$_{17}$Cl
6	$_{21}$Sc	$_{23}$V
7	$_{25}$Mn	$_{29}$Cu
8	$_{27}$Co	$_{31}$Ga
9	$_{33}$As	$_{35}$Br
10	$_{39}$Y	$_{37}$Rb
11	$_{41}$Nb	$_{47}$Ag
12	$_{45}$Rh	$_{49}$In
13	$_{53}$I	$_{51}$Sb
14	$_{55}$Cs	$_{57}$La
15	$_{59}$Pr	$_{63}$Eu
16	$_{65}$Tb	$_{71}$Lu
17	$_{67}$Ho	$_{73}$Ta
18	$_{69}$Tm	$_{75}$Re
19	$_{79}$Au	$_{77}$Ir
20	$_{83}$Bi	$_{81}$Tl

forty even-numbered elements of the Periodic Table into 1 + 19 tables. I was now convinced that the 81 stable elements obeyed a quadruple expansion: **4 × (1+19)**. Further thoughts on this subject can be found in the other books I have already published.

As shown in the table of the 81 stable elements on page 33, the elements from 1 to 20 are a prime group of elements. From element 21 on, the inclusion of electrons in lower shells begins. The lack of information about why this is the case is normally hushed up and disguised by spectacular measurement results.

These processes in the electron shells are accompanied by parallel processes in the atomic nucleus of which only a few chemists and physicists are aware. The first 20 atomic nuclei follow a rule that relates to the additional inclusion of neutrons and that does not need to be explained further here.

From element 21 on, each atomic nucleus contains more neutrons than protons. For the uneven-numbered elements 21 to 83, additional neutrons and different quantities in each case are appended on top of the normal neutrons corresponding to the number of protons. This follows in accordance with precise rules: the element 21 has three additional neutrons and thus has an atomic weight of 45 (21+21+3). The element 83 contains 43 additional neutrons, and for the even-numbered elements similar rules apply.

In all, from element 21 to element 83 (omitting the elements 43 and 61) 61 elements thus hold increasingly high numbers of neutrons.

Until then, nobody had given an explanation why higher elements have a disproportionate number of neutrons. Moreover, neutrons tend to evade experimental investigation because they have no charge. This is why the very existence of the neutron was only proved in 1932. At that time there was general euphoria over the notion that the neutron was a fusion of the negatively-charged electron and the positively-charged proton. It was possible to use this knowledge in the construction of atomic bombs and power stations. And we all know the price we had to pay for that discovery.

The true significance of the third atomic particle has never been connected to the notion of numbers, or even to the charge number 0. It was not thought proper to link the essence of the neutral nucleic component to numbers and quantity since the prevailing opinion was that numbers can only be a coincidence.

Numbers are conventionally categorized into even and uneven numbers. Conventional logic also prohibits a number from being both even and uneven. Every investigation of nuclear laws according to number theory would have to fail. The additional neutrons without which the nuclei could not be stable led to similar difficulties, in the case of the atomic shells, over how equally-charged electrons can come together to form pairs. In the atomic nucleus similarly-charged protons also link up, as in reality should not happen.

A new theory had to be invented – one which could scarcely be more embarrassing: the 'glue theory'. The explanation is given in all seriousness by professors and receivers of the Nobel Prize throughout the world that the additional neutrons prevent the nucleus from falling apart. One should imagine them as a type of glue.

The appalling scandal of such a theory is easily exposed in the case of the final stable element. It is stable with 43 extra neutrons, but with 42 and 44 neutrons it is unstable. Similar cases can be found for many other elements.

Further investigation of the 81 stable elements in the Periodic Table – without the element 19 – from the point of view of number theory resulted in 57 elements; ie 3 times 19 have divisible atomic numbers and the remaining 19 have prime atomic numbers. After I had discovered the 3 + 1 law as the foundation of the Prime Number Cross in 1980, and had thus created the conditions necessary to cast some light into the dark recesses of the electrons shell, I now found the same (3 + 1) plan in the atomic nucleus. The law thus centres on 4 times (1 + 19).

This law would not be fulfilled if two prime number elements had not been barred from taking part in natural existence.

I had now finally solved the question why two prime number elements in the periodic system should be missing. In 1986 I finally managed to prove why these two missing elements should happen to be the elements with the atomic numbers 43 and 61. The proof is rigorously mathematical, and critics will have to admit that the problem would never have been solved with conventional chemistry and physics.

NOTE
1 The original calculation (1795) of the metre (one 10,000,000th of the distance between the North Pole and the equator) means that this system is directly linked to the natural constants.

CHAPTER TWELVE

THE HOUSE OF CARDS THAT IS PHYSICS

I had long been wondering about the expression π, which has the value 3.14159 .... Along with the Euler number e, it is the most important mathematical constant and occurs in physical equations and in physical natural constants with an amazingly precise 'coincidence' again and again.

The area of a circle with a radius of 1 centimetre is 3.141 ... square centimetres. It is normal in mathematics to agree on a radius of 1 and not to set a dimension in centimetres (figure 5).

The surface of a sphere with a diameter of the circle measures exactly four times this dimension – ie 4π. Most people are not familiar with this elegant formula for calculation, but whoever knows the formula for the surface of a sphere should actually ask why the beautiful even number 4 should occur here and not some decimal fraction. The proof provided by Archimedes in the 3rd century before Christ does not throw much light on the mystery itself either.

Geometrically, the relationship between a square (of surface area 4×1^2) and the surface area of its inner circle with a radius 1 is the ratio $4:\pi$.

$$4 : \pi = 1.2732 \ldots$$

The relationship of a quarter of this square with the area 1^2 to a quarter of the circle $4:\pi$ has therefore the same value: 1.2732 ...

I now examined the relationship of a surface of a single

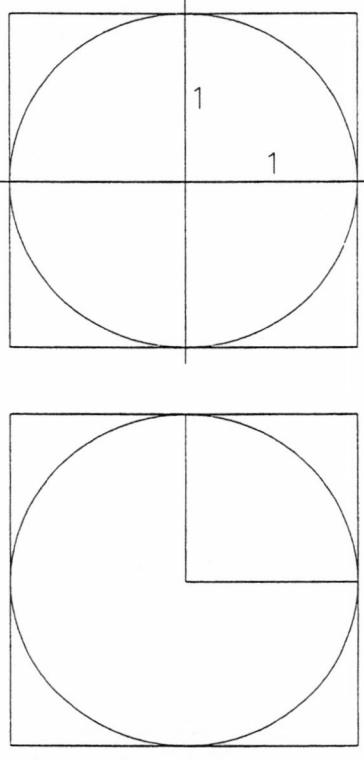

Figure 5

cornered cap to the quarter-circle lying underneath. To my astonishment, the result was now a decimal sequence of numbers which was precisely 1 less than the above and which had been familiar to me since my youth as the sequence of figures of the sidereal month (27.32 days): 0.2732 ....

The exact calculation is:

$$(1-\frac{\pi}{4}): \frac{\pi}{4} = \frac{4}{\pi} - 1 = \frac{4-\pi}{\pi} = 0.2732 \ldots$$

The ratio of these two areas is a mathematical constant that has so far been unknown in mathematics. The corner is actually the flapped up centre of the circle (figure 6). Both points constitute the central axis when the circle rotates.

This made me think that this mathematical constant might be another physical constant of nature which was as yet unnamed.

138

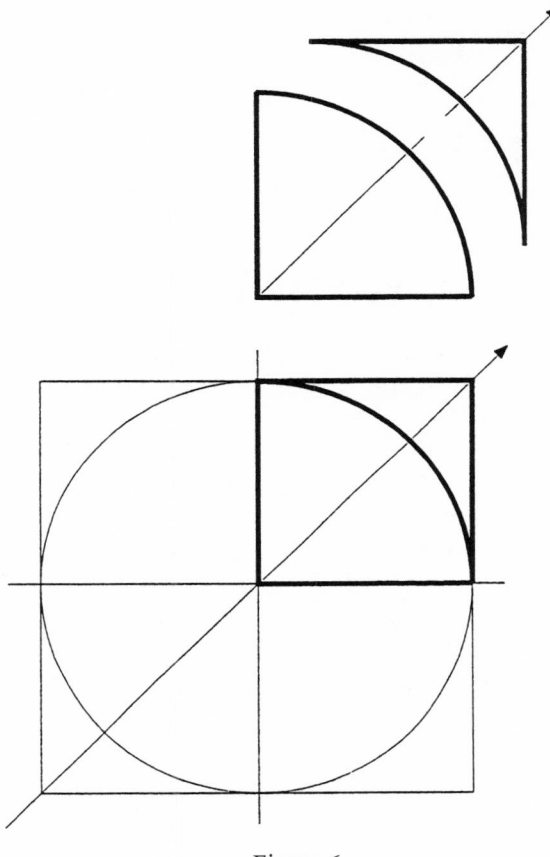

Figure 6

All at once the Earth-Moon system again assumed a central significance in my thoughts.

The Earth is the third planet of the solar system. The distance between the Earth and the sun is roughly 150 million kilometres (92 million miles). If this distance were either 1 per cent less or 1 per cent greater no life on our planet would be possible. How nice for us that it should be just the right distance!

The length of an Earth-year measures approximately 365.25 days. Because we count 365 days for 3 years, we have to count 366 days for 1 year. This natural 3 + 1 law is not affected by the fact that every 400 years a further day must be added.

But could these durations of orbit – 27.32 days for the Moon and 366 days per leap year for the Earth – be only an expression

139

of the reciprocal connection between these dual planets? When these fractions are worked out, they confirm the suspicion exactly to the fourth decimal place:

$$\frac{1}{27.32} = 0.03660 \ldots$$

and

$$\frac{1}{366} = 0.002732 \ldots$$

Because the distance between the Earth and the sun is scarcely a coincidence, I found the reciprocal correlation of the times of orbit of the Earth and Moon fascinating. It was a crime of literally astronomical proportions to hide this fact from the public – just because nothing could be allowed to exist that should not exist. And I was certainly not the first to notice it either! It seemed that nobody had had enough courage to publish a fact which could cast doubt on the power of coincidence.

I searched for two further astronomical values, the acceleration of the Moon in its path around the Earth, and the radius of the Moon. The acceleration is measured as

$$0.273 \times \frac{cm}{s^2}$$

and the Moon radius measures

$$0.272 \text{ Earth radii}$$

My suspicion was that an examination of these numbers would again produce the value 0.273.

And in fact the acceleration of the Earth and the Moon behave reciprocally as the squares of the radii of the orbits of Earth and Moon. This was interpreted by physicists only as a brilliant confirmation of Newton's law of gravity.

I had always considered the Moon to be the Earth's smaller co-planet. What is the relationship between the mass of the Moon and that of the Earth? I looked it up. The ratio is **1:81**. The ratio 1 to 81 is written mathematically as $1/81 = 0.0123$.

So there it was again, the 3^4 law. In relation to the aforementioned astronomical data, it is totally impossible that the Moon is a body from somewhere else out in the universe only captured by the Earth as a satellite by chance. I felt that everybody on this planet really ought to know this fact.

I had to think back to one special day in the Institute for Nuclear Chemistry when I became one of the first chemists in Germany to touch the glassy black sand from the Moon. When I touched it, I instinctively brought my index finger to my mouth, taking some grains of the sand on my finger into my mouth before swallowing the Moon dust, under the incredulous stare of Professor Herr. I now knew why I had behaved unconsciously in this way.

The distance, size and path of the three heavenly bodies, the **Sun**, the **Earth** and the **Moon**, are arranged ingeniously from an astronomical point of view. That eclipses can occur at all while these bodies move in their courses is a wonder. The diameter of the Earth, Moon and sun, and their relative distances from each other are such that the sun (which is much larger) takes up the same space in our view as the Moon. And this is why these three spheres cover each other for a short time in a total eclipse. The best Swiss watchmaker could not have worked with greater precision. In earlier times astronomers gave a lot of thought to this incredible 'coincidence'.

The reason these eclipses occur only periodically is the rise and fall of the Moon in the course of its orbit around the Earth, of which most people are not aware. After every 18 years and 11.33 days (6,585.78 days) this eclipse arrangement recurs with the greatest precision.

It can easily be calculated[1] to show that such a cycle corresponds to a whole number of eclipse years. The relationship between 6,585.78 days and the length of an eclipse year measuring 346.62 days is

$$6585.78 : 346.62 = 19$$

eclipse years.

The Saros cycle of a total of 8 eclipse occurrences in exactly 19 eclipse years was known to all advanced cultures, including the ancient Celts and Nordic Germanic races. Today it is not considered important enough to tell our high-school students. The prime number 19 and its relation to the Moon is not even considered significant by the very few scientists who are aware of the fact. Otherwise they would have to admit that it is not a

141

coincidence.

At the beginning of 1984 I suddenly decided to speak to some clever scientist about the results of my work, for I considered an external judgement to be important as a form of monitoring.

While I was considering who might be the most suitable person, I suddenly remembered that on two occasions I had already indirectly met an inorganic chemist who was also the recipient of the Nobel Prize – Professor E O Fischer, who was the first to synthesize a chemical compound with a zerovalent metal atom.

I took up the phone and called the Technische Hochschule in Munich and asked for Professor Fischer. I then told him briefly about events in Cologne and my current ideas on the porphyrin ring of haemes as quadrupole magnets. Professor Fischer answered with the voice of excitement that only a passionate chemist has when he hears something new. My idea was the most astounding he had ever heard in his life. I then told him how many years I had been trying to get behind the secret of the two missing elements of the Periodic Table, which had always appeared to me to be something of a mute warning but which had been very cleverly avoided by our thick textbooks.

'Are you telling me, Mr Plichta, that you have discovered something in this field? As you know, the elements are the basis of all science.'

'Yes,' I said, 'except that the solution is of a kind that is totally different from the one any chemist would expect. It is linked to the basics of mathematics, the prime numbers, and the geometry of space. What I have discovered is in fact very simple, although nobody is prepared for it. I have called you because you are the holder of the Nobel Prize. With you I at least have the chance of being objectively assessed.'

'Mr Plichta, nothing much is being done in chemistry at the moment with regard to the fundamental, major questions. Scarcely anybody any more can even hold all of chemistry in his head. Perhaps it is true that only a person like you, who has studied all three natural sciences, can find new solutions.' After a short hesitation, he continued: 'Have you ever heard of Professor Böhme in Marburg? He is called the Pope of Pharmacy.'

'Yes,' I replied, moved by the way this conversation was

going. 'I know him well. As president of the state examination board of Hesse he gave me the top grade with four stars in the state pharmacy examination.'

On the night of 17 January I took the night train to Munich. At exactly 2pm I stepped into Professor Fischer's office. We shook hands before sitting down on a small couch.

'Please begin, Mr Plichta.'

'May I assume that it is a total mystery to you why radioactivity begins after element 83.'

'Yes, you may. I know that my colleagues do not talk of mysteries any more.'

I was relieved and told him of my year-long study of the triple aspect of nature and the 3^4 law I had discovered. I then sketched how easy it is to get from the $1 + 19$ pure isotopes to the 4 times $(1 + 19)$ elements.

Professor Fischer understood. He became more and more excited. I now told him about the four groups of divisible elements before going on to the $3 + 1$ problem and thus to the prime numbers. I outlined my belief that at some time in the future the Pythagorean notion that everything is number and Kepler's notion that everything is geometry would finally be accepted.

'Natural science fought the great scientist John Dalton for a hundred years, and he did nothing more than take up the ideas of Leukipp and Democritus. At the end of this shameful dispute it was clear that not only matter but also energy is in fact made up of single units according to the whole numbers 1, 2, 3 ...'

We had thus arrived at Einstein's equation and the factor 81. Professor Fischer reacted with shock when I told him that the reciprocal values for these numbers result from our number series, and that in my opinion space is not only numerical space but the fact is that the geometry of this space must bear a relation to the decimal system.

'Without the invention of the decimal system, mathematics, natural science and technology would be unimaginable today. At the same time, the history of the discovery of decimal calculation – I mean the decimal fraction method – is discussed neither in schools nor in universities. Its introduction by Simon Stevin immediately gave people the possibility of working out fractions, expressing the number π, constructing measuring apparatus, and so on. The decimal system to which we owe so much is considered by mathematicians to be only one of the possible models.

The real significance of this system as a framework for construction, as the basic methodology of the universe, is not even suspected. Very shortly after the decimal system was introduced, the logarithm was invented, which allowed Kepler to prove Copernicus' theories with great precision. Moreover, the door was then thrown open to the invention of differential calculus, the fourth mode of calculation.'

Professor Fischer interrupted me: 'Mr Plichta, you are quite right. The triple aspect of nature which you point out so strongly was discovered at least five thousand years ago by Egyptian priests, and later surfaced in our notion of the trinity of God.'

I now changed the subject to the building-blocks of life, to the triple nature of DNA, to the quadruple nature of bases, and I explained to him how it could be inferred from my experimental investigations of disilane and digermanium that the 19 left-oriented amino acids did not become the building-blocks of life simply by chance. I drew the structural formula for the two amino acids with double asymmetrical centres, which from a stereochemical point of view require that only a quarter of the 80 stereochemical combinations are anchored in the plan of life.

I had now been speaking for two hours. We took a break. Professor Fischer walked briskly up and down the room. He appeared euphoric and his movements displayed something of the balletic. We then continued.

Using pencil and paper I derived for him the reciprocal orbiting dimensions of the Earth and the Moon, behind which there is nothing else but the 3^4 law and the relationship of a quarter segment of a circle (an infinite corner) to a single corner.

'Life on this planet is maintained by three chemical ring systems in whose centre three different metallic atoms are located. Your discovery of zerovalent chromium atoms has already got you a Nobel Prize. Perhaps with your synthesizing work you have really opened the door to deciphering the secret of life itself. How would it be if iron did not happen to be in haemoglobin? How would it be if the magnesium atom in the living chlorophyll is not bivalent, as is assumed, but rather zerovalent and could thus periodically split water molecules? The production of negatively-charged hydrogen would then be explained. Sunlight would provide the energy for changing the charge of the magnesium atom. Nature would then be quite ingeniously arranged and not simply a product of chance through evolution. Our entire scientific edifice would collapse overnight.'

'Hold on a moment, Mr Plichta. You don't need to convince me any more. I am perfectly satisfied with your explanation that with the omission of the two non-existent elements, the Periodic Table now consists of 81 elements and thus of four groups according to the sequence 1 + 19. If that is in fact the case, it will be quite sufficient to place all of contemporary science in an impossible position. But we have to be careful. New ideas have always been resisted. This one is not merely a new and revolutionary idea, it actually turns our entire concept of the universe on its head!'

I interrupted him: 'If the world can be saved, then it will be saved only by a new spiritual idea. If I can prove that the number 3 and the decimal system are at the basis of the speed of light, then we could overcome the danger of the bomb. War is an expression of our fear. Fear is based on ignorance. We shall simply have to go right through with presenting it at the political level. Any disputes we may encounter with the academic world will, in contrast, look harmless.'

Professor Fischer had become very thoughtful. He suddenly said to me, 'I have known for years that you would come to me one day.' He then told me a story.

As a young man, I was an officer at the front in Russia. Then, when I returned, everything I had believed in was acknowledged to be false. I had intended to study the only thing I had ever wanted – chemistry – but the situation for a student of chemistry was a disaster. There was, however, among my acquaintances a certain winner of the Nobel Prize, Johannes Stark, who during the Nazi period had not been kind to his Jewish colleagues, to put it mildly. He had helped drive the Jewish scientists from Germany under Hitler, but had now been dismissed himself after the tide had turned.

He was the son of a prosperous farmer and had set up a laboratory in a barn where he now gave private lessons. I visited him there one day. He told me that I should definitely go on studying. It was not important that the situation in Germany was so bad. It was not so important that he was no longer a professor. What was important was the answer to the major questions of physics. He had made mistakes. His fight against Jewish physics should, however, not be confused with what the Nazi murderers had wanted and had carried out. His fight for physics had been the result of his passion for truth. In the coming years, the triumph would belong to those whom he had helped drive into exile. Quantum mechanics would be developed into a citadel. It was totally pointless trying to fight it.

'But one day, young man – perhaps it will take 30 or 40 years – someone will come, some one with an individual mind, and then modern physics will collapse like a house of cards. For what I fought with such passion, I fought because it was wrong. I am a physicist, I have been awarded the Nobel Prize, and I know that modern physics is wrong.'

Years passed. One day I was standing in Stockholm and was awarded the famous prize which Herr Stark had also been awarded. My mind returned to that conversation. Everything had happened as Stark had predicted. The major questions of science had been forgotten, and chemistry had become merely an auxiliary science to physics.

I am going to retire soon. Now, at the end of my scientific life, the door has suddenly opened and that individual someone is standing in front of me.

We were silent for a moment. Now I was the one who was moved.

'Professor Stark must have known that what happens in the atomic nuclei has nothing to do with chance. It only looks that way. And a person's destiny, such as mine, can also not be a coincidence, even if it often looks that way. I was born a twin and later worked with twin atoms, and even later with twin electron pairs. I have now come to primary number twins, but we can talk about that some other time.'

That evening he drove me to my hotel. He appeared totally exhausted. We took solemn leave of each other.

'Mr Plichta, I shall get in touch with a physicist. There is one here in Munich who is also a holder of the Nobel Prize – Professor Rudolf Mössbauer.'

I stood alone in front of the hotel entrance. Whatever

happened now, I had achieved everything I wanted. A high-ranking chemist had immediately grasped the inplications of my ideas and had assured me that I was on the right track. How different would things have been if this man, whom I had chosen as if moved by the hand of fate, had shown nothing but incomprehension? How would I then have proceeded? But as it happened, I had not only obtained the support of Professor Fischer but I had also been inspired by those second-hand words of Professor Stark.

The next day I returned to Düsseldorf. I wanted to continue my research with all the power at my command, but suddenly I did not want to do it alone. I needed a female companion, a fellow scientist with whom I could share my daily life and also pursue my scientific interests. I was now 44 years old and had lived as a recluse for too long.

'If I cannot find her,' I said aloud, so that God could not help but hear me, 'then He will have to find someone else to do His work.'

One day, around noon, at the end of January, I received a telephone call from Professor Fischer. His voice sounded very agitated.

'Mr Plichta, I have been in touch with Mr Mössbauer and told him that the two of us wanted to introduce him to something new, and that there was some need for caution in this regard. He wanted to know whether your discovery would raise doubts about quantum mechanics. I told him that quantum mechanics would not even exist if what you discovered turned out to be true. Quantum mechanics would then simply turn out to be a figment of the imagination. My colleague Mössbauer then got very angry and accused me of putting everything we have accomplished at risk. Our great achievement, modern physics, was the result of tremendous efforts, and now everything would collapse should any doubts arise. Such people as yourself should not be given support under any circumstances. He refuses to meet you. He does not even want to hear any of the new ideas. He gave me a very serious warning indeed.'

I could have laughed. Instead I said calmly, 'We don't need Professor Mössbauer at all. It would be better to consult a third chemist.' I was thinking of Professor Böhme.

'No, Mr Plichta. In the circumstances I'm afraid I cannot help you. You will have to continue by yourself. Please do not be angry with me. I wish you all the best.'

'Professor, I am not angry with you. You have really helped me. I needed your expert opinion. But now your job is done. I wish you too all the best for the future.'

When I had replaced the telephone receiver I was overwhelmed with fury. I shouted out, 'Everything collapse, Professor Mössbauer? How right you are!'

At the end of February 1984, I met Christina Burckhard. She was 37 years old and had just received her doctorate. She had formerly studied philosophy, German and history, and had been a teacher for some time. In our first conversation, I immediately perceived with elation that I would be able to talk to her all I wanted to about left-oriented amino acids and other things that were important to me. She decided not to take up her profession but instead to support me in my work.

So the 'Lord above' would not need to look for somebody else after all.

NOTE
1 A Unsöld, *Der Neue Kosmos*, Berlin, 1974; p 22.

CHAPTER THIRTEEN

THE LAW OF EMPTY SPACE

On the morning of 6 December 1984, I was studying, as I had many times before, the Prime Number Cross (figure 4, page 120) and concepts of number theory.

I made a few calculations. Suddenly something occurred to me as if from a half-forgotten memory. I left the desk, walked across the room, moved about and stood in the centre of the room. When I stretched out my hand, I suddenly appreciated the full significance of my calculations.

'I have discovered something about the essence of the speed of light,' I said to myself in wonder.

When people occupy themselves with mathematics, especially higher mathematics, the abstract meaning of numbers is generally in the foreground. In daily life too – eg when we look at price tags or read the time on a clock – we seldom think that the figures are only an abstract symbol for a certain amount. The number 8, for example, is the name for a set comprising eight elements, such as grains of rice. Under this quantitative aspect I now considered the first numerical circle of the Prime Number Cross which contains the numbers from 0 to 24. The sum of the numbers 1 to 24 gives the value 300 exactly.

When I added the numbers on the second circle I arrived at the total 876. I immediately realized that exactly 24 was missing to make the round number 900. Should I perhaps therefore begin with 24 and not with 25 when counting the second circle?

I played with the idea of counting 25 numbers on each circle. The point of intersection between the two circles is counted twice as a starting and final number. I obtained the following values:

$$
\begin{array}{lll}
\text{1st circle:} & 0 + 1 + 2 \ldots + 24 = & 300 = 1 \times 300 \\
\text{2nd circle:} & 24 + 25 + 26 \ldots + 48 = & 900 = 3 \times 300 \\
\text{3rd circle:} & 48 + 49 + 50 \ldots + 72 = & 1{,}500 = 5 \times 300 \\
\text{4th circle:} & 72 + 73 + 74 \ldots + 96 = & 2{,}100 = 7 \times 300 \\
& \text{etc.} &
\end{array}
$$

The basic value 300 clearly increased over the sequence of uneven numbers 1, 3, 5, 7, 9, 11, ... This was certainly related to the law of uneven numbers, and had been known even to Pythagoras.

As a schoolboy I had noticed when looking at tiled walls that squares of tiles follow a certain law of multiplication.

If you start with *one* square tile, the next largest square is achieved by adding three tiles at one corner. The square now consists of four tiles. If a further five tiles are added at one of the corners, the result is an even larger square consisting of nine tiles. The next tiled squares have 16, 25, 36 tiles, and so on. The sum of these uneven numbers of added tiles 1, 3, 5, 7, 9, 11, ... always gives a series of squared numbers beginning with 1^2. This is followed by $1 + 3 = 4 = 2^2$, then $1 + 3 + 5 = 9 = 3^2$, then $1 + 3 + 5 + 7 = 16 = 4^2$, and so on.

The first uneven number gives 1^2. If the first two uneven numbers are added the result is 2^2. The sum of the first three uneven numbers gives 3^2 and of the first four uneven numbers gives 4^2, and so on.

The simplicity and elegance of this law is not taught in our schools. If it were, it would be possible to make the most important law of physics, Newton's reciprocal square law, comprehensible even to ten-year-olds. This does not involve any complicated material normally taught in universities, but only the presentation of amazing insights into the numerical background of the universe.

In all operations with numbers arranged on the circles of the Prime Number Cross, this quadratic law is maintained (see figure 7).

If the numbers 0, 1, 2, 3, 4, 5 on the first circle are added, the

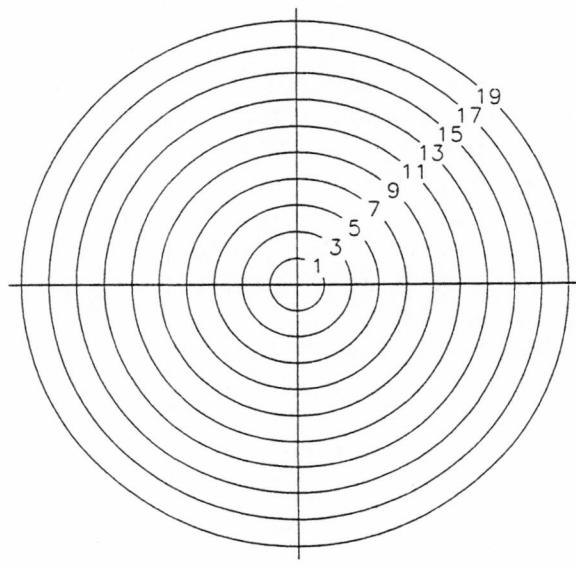

Figure 7

basic value 300 is achieved. This basic value corresponds to one tile in our example. To be mathematically correct it is 300 x 1^2. Because the sum of the numbers on the second circle is 900, the total for the first and second circle together is 300 + 900 = 1,200, ie 300 x 2^2. The sum of the numbers on the first three circles measures 300 + 900 + 1,500 = 2,700. This corresponds to 300 x 3^2.

The enlargement of the number quantities (sums) on the circles on the Prime Number Cross thus run through the product of the basic value 300 with the square numbers 1^2, 2^2, 3^2, 4^2, ...

By these square numbers the number of electron twins on the atomic shell also increases.

Everything we know about the atom was discovered by observation and meticulous experiment. The Prime Number Cross corresponds to this atomic model and provides the theoretical background. What better proof for the real existence of numbers could one wish for?

I gradually became infused with the overwhelming notion that the basic value 300 and its expansion through the square of the natural numbers could lead to a solution to the problem of the speed of light.

151

The Prime Number Cross consists of the infinite sequence of cardinal numbers (0, 1, 2, 3, ...) arranged on concentric circles. From circle to circle the (numerical) total extends by means of the squares of this continuous, ordered number sequence (1^2, 2^2, 3^2, 4^2, ...).

Just as the totals increase on the expanded circles through the added uneven numbers, so conversely the energy of an electromagnetic wave expanding through space decreases as the radius increases, exactly according to the reciprocal squares of the natural numbers.

The sum of the first ten uneven expanding numbers is:

$$1 + 3 + 5 + 7 + 9 + 11 + 13 + 15 + 17 + 19 = 100 = 10^2$$

When the group of the next ten uneven expanding numbers is added –

$$21 + 23 + 25 + 27 + 29 + 31 + 33 + 35 + 37 + 39 = 300$$

it becomes clear that the sum of these ten numbers results in *three times* the sum of the numbers 1, 3, 5, ... 19.

The sum of the next group of ten, the uneven numbers 41, 43, 45, ... 69 results in *five times* the sum of the first ten uneven numbers.

Once, three times, five times, seven times, etc. of the first ten number circles therefore makes up a higher order of expanding numbers.

It is a help at this stage to look once more at the example of the grains of rice. The basic number of 300 hundred grains of rice on the first numerical circle increases to

$$300 \times 100 = 300 \times 10^2 = 30,000$$

after going through the first ten shells. After running through the next ten circles, our 300 grains of rice are no longer multiplied by 100 but already by 300. We obtain 90,000 grains of rice. On the next ten circles we multiply by 500 and obtain 150,000 grains of rice. When we pass on to the next level, the grains of rice for all ten circles must be added together. We then obtain for $10 \times 10 = 100$ circles a total of rice grains amounting to $300 \times 100 \times 100$. This makes 3,000,000. The basic sum of 300 on the first circle in the Prime Number Cross can itself be shown as a product of the number 100: **3 × 100**.

The basic factor 3, the constant of the Prime Number Cross, is simply increased by 100s, by the squares of the number 10.

$$3 \times 10^2 \times 10^2 \times 10^2 \ldots$$

We find ourselves in a base 100 system, or – since 100 is the square of 10 – in the *decimal system*.

Because infinity has a triple nature – space, time and number – the numbers themselves evolve on the basis of the first three numbers – 1, 2 and 3 – and the basic constant of the Prime Number Cross is the number 3, the expansion constant of the speed of light must also be 3.

I was now suddenly capable of revolutionizing our notion of the speed of light. I had discovered the error in reasoning which we make when we speak of the speed of the electromagnetic wave.

A shining star or a burning candle appear to us as points of light, approaching us directly as a beam of light. In reality, shining objects are permanently emitting spheroid waves which diminish as they approach infinity with a fixed consistency through the reciprocal square law. It would be a mental cul-de-sac to describe this process as speed. Speed in the physical sense is linked to matter. When an atom, a football or a space rocket flies from A to B, it takes place at a certain speed that is physically established as a calculation of distance over time.

With such a notion of speed used in physics, we have attempted to tackle the measurement of light expansion without pausing to consider that electromagnetic waves are not matter. An object can be accelerated or braked. Light itself cannot be made to travel more slowly or more quickly. It can only lose its intensity by expanding through space.

Our investigation of the speed of light was undertaken with the same yardsticks we normally use to measure the speed of objects – in the way the speed of a car is measured by a police radar or a 100-metre sprinter is measured on a stopwatch. We have in the meantime been able to measure the speed of light to many places after the decimal point. The precision of these findings actually prevents us from the realization that we do not know why the speed of light should be so consistent. For scientists the results of measurements are the true reality.

Healthy scepticism should always assume that what we see or measure may be an illusion.

We see an intensive searchlight as a band of light. We do not register the speed, or even movement. If, on the other hand, we measure the speed of a beam of light going to the Moon and back, we are actually measuring a period of time. The fact that in this process the light diminishes greatly in intensity is simply 'compensated for' by intensifier gauges. And thus the diminution itself gives us the impression of speed.

An oscillating electron transmits electromagnetic waves because it carries a charge. The waves of an unimaginably large number of electrons in a glowing wire are physically added in four-dimensional space. We see the wire glowing. The notion that the wire is emitting photons or 'packets of waves' is naive.

In our imagination we can conceive space in which 100 long-wave radio transmitters, 100 medium-wave radio transmitters, 100 short-wave transmitters, 100 ultra-short-wave transmitters and 100 radar stations are operating. At the same time there should be enough channels left for 100 two-way radio sets, and the same number of microwave and infra-red devices. The same space should also have 100 coloured flashlight sets, and the same number of ultra-violet and X-ray machines. In addition we might add 100 more transmitters of gamma waves. All are transmitting electromagnetic waves which differ only in their number of oscillations (energy). Space will have no problem handling such an apparent mess of waves. It transports all information with the greatest precision – by virtue of its Prime Number Structure. This basic fact had not been realized before.

The speed of light we measure has the finite value of almost exactly 3×10^{10} centimetres per second. The newly discovered constant for numerical expansion for infinite numerical space around every possible point in infinity cannot be finite but has the infinite value of

$$3 \times 10^n$$

totals of numbers by which an electromagnetic effect diminishes as it approaches infinity according to the reciprocal square law. Because the speed of light requires the measurements centimetre and second for its physical definition and the constant of numeric expansion (3×10^n) is without dimensions,

154

the difficult question arises as to why in both cases the factor 3 is identical.

The significance of the absolute number 1 can also not be reduced by the objection that centimetres and seconds are arbitrary measurement sizes. They are not. The metre was established according to a decimal division of the Earth's axial circumference. The second was derived from the speed of the Earth's rotation.

Whoever has carefully read the previous chapter and is thus aware of the relationship between the astronomical data of the Earth and of the Moon will know that the two heavenly bodies are mathematically linked with the greatest degree of precision. Because nobody was present to form these spheres with his hands, to bring them to the correct distance and to start them at reciprocal orbiting numbers, the only explanation left is that nature is in itself intelligent and we human beings as self-reflecting creatures are the self-realization of this intelligence.

The metric system for length and weight and our time system are both expressed according to the decimal system. In the past we were obliged to introduce a standard symbol to end the international confusion caused by the various measurements of length and weight. The fact that we 'by coincidence' hit on the very system in which nature, and we ourselves, are created is quite clearly not a coincidence at all but is the result only of logical consistency. Nature asserted itself!

I can now finally tackle the question of why the Bohr model of the atom demands that the first shell may be occupied by only two electrons while the subsequent inert gas shells – I mean the last one in each case – always have to have eight electrons.

On every shell of the Prime Number Cross, there is the same amount of numbers. The amount of 'rice grains' is, however, different on each level. There is a quantitative magnitude according to the squares of the whole numbers.

From element 20 onwards, the integration of additional electrons occurs on the shells. The reasons for this could never be provided by quantum mechanics, which explained this fact as representing the leap of electrons from shell to shell.

Figure 8 shows the Prime Number Cross with the squares of

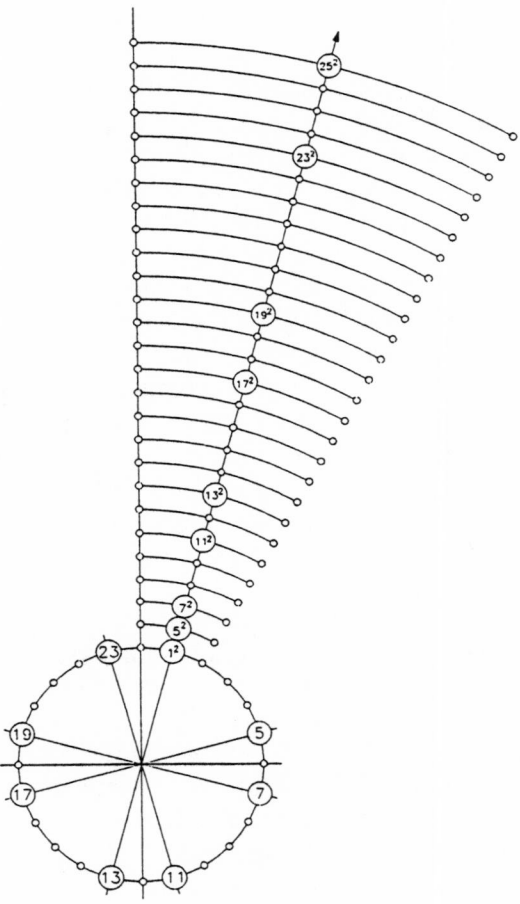

Figure 8

the numbers in which it itself is coded.

$$1^2, 5^2, 7^2, 11^2, 13^2, 17^2, 19^2, 23^2 \ldots$$

The question of why the squares of the prime numbers on the orbits all have to be located in order on the first beam is simple to answer. Mathematically speaking the Prime Number Cross is a factorial-4 cross:

$$1 \times 2 \times 3 \times 4 = 24 \ (= 4!)$$

Such products of the multiplication of whole numbers in a series starting with 1 are referred to as factorials and are indicated by an exclamation mark (!) which can sometimes be very confusing.

All multiples of the number 24 and thus all factorials are therefore located on the ray above the 24.

If the number 1 is added to one of these multiples – let's take as an example 48 – the value 49 is obtained, which is 7^2. This square number of a prime number of the form $6n \pm 1$ is situated on the ray running through the 1. All other prime number squares are also situated on this ray. If, however, all squares of the prime numbers are on this ray, the first number must itself be squared – therefore 1^2 instead of 1 (figure 8).

Since 1980 six years had passed in which I had been unable to close a gap to the first shell to the right beside the number -1 on the Primary Number Cross (figure 4, page 120). And now I had solved this problem. I placed the number 1 below the number 1^2.

The special thing about the number 1 is that it is itself a squared number. The mathematical calculation is

$$(-1)^2 = +1$$

This number $+1$ stands opposite the number -1 as in a space mirror, as illustrated in figure 9.

The prophecy had therefore been fulfilled that I would decipher the Planck-Einstein relation. I had created a model that confirmed Bohr's fundamental idea in atomic physics. The atomic nucleus has become the centre of the Prime Number Cross. Space is arranged around this point in the form of shells. The four prime number twins of the first shell determine the structure of all further shells and demand a zero shell on which only the numbers $+1$ and -1 are situated. It had formerly been a total mystery why the atomic shells have to have a lower shell on which only two electrons are located.

I postulated why a shell-shaped numerical space around the atomic nucleus would hold electrons, although I was not aware of the precise reason for such adherence. When energy is received – by heating – an electron changes its place and jumps to a higher shell. When it again falls back to the lower shell it emits its energy in the form of two wave segments which are at right-angles to each other (sine and cosine of a spherical wave). The oscillating electron thus becomes the central point of a

157

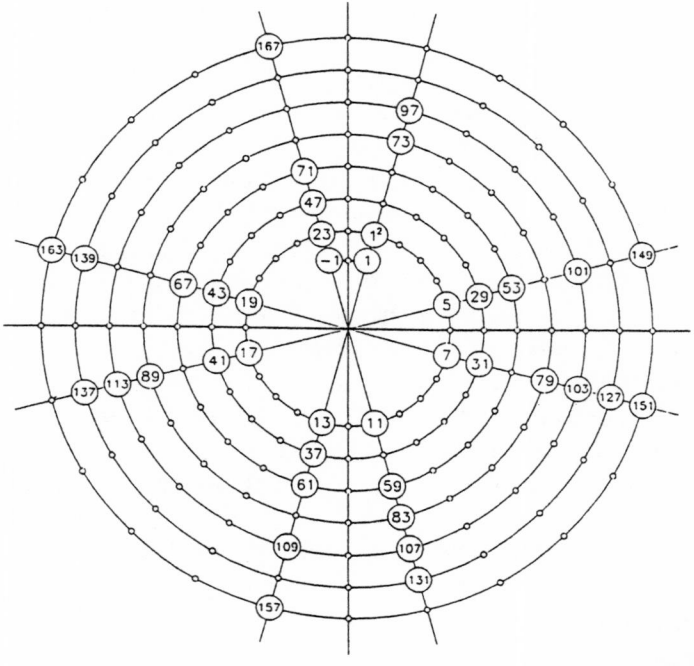

Figure 9

four-dimensional infinite space. The expanding wave must therefore race towards infinity with the base factor 3.

Bohr, Planck and Einstein were all unable to tell us anything about the reasons for the shelled structure of the electrons around the atomic nucleus and for the absolute value of the natural constants h^1 and c and their connections. Their successors were certainly no better. I had now established with certainty that physics would be confronted with questions that it could not solve as long as it did not recognize the true structure of space. This is what had to be studied next.

NOTE

1 My solution for the absolute value of the quantum of action h and the nuclear angular momentum $h/4\pi$ can be found in my book *The Prime Number Cross*. It is a strange fact that protons, electrons and neutrons have the same nuclear angular momentum. The theory of a rotating particle must be abandoned.

CHAPTER FOURTEEN

REVELATION

When investigating the problems of the Prime Number Cross I had always found occasion to draw on the image of the grains of rice to illustrate the quantitative expansion of the numbers. But now the main focus of my attention was on investigating combinational numbers.

On the first full circle of the Prime Number Cross, the numbers 0, 2, 3, ... 24 are placed as on a 24-hour clock. One says when glancing at such a clock that it is, let us say, ten o'clock. But by 'ten o'clock' we mean that ten hours of the day have already passed. One could perhaps more properly say that one hour has passed ten times. It is just the same with the Prime Number Cross. The ten means the same as ten times one. However, because I had proved that the number 1^2 should actually take the place of the one, the true reading should actually be 10×1^2.

The number 5^2 is above the number 1^2. Where is the number 5×5^2? This number, 125, is on the ray that begins with 5. Two other examples. Where is the number 29×13^2? It is on the ray beginning with 5, 29, 53, etc. And the product of $13 \times 17^2 \times 29^2$ must be on the ray that begins with 13. On the position where the number 1^2 stands, therefore, the expression 1×1^2 should actually stand. Because of this, all numbers on the Prime Number Cross are products with the number 1^2.

The Prime Number Cross is in reality a rotating numerical

cross. To return to our 'ten o'clock' example: with the number 10, the 1^2 has moved forward ten positions. Actually only one single number turns in each case: $1^2 = (+1)^2$.

When it has reached the number 24, it jumps to the next shell over the 25. Because $+1$ is itself the product of $(-1) \times (-1)$, we may now write the number 1^2 as follows:

$$1^2 = (-1)^4$$

The numbers on the individual shells therefore mean two times, three times, four times up to infinity times the mathematical expression $(-1)^4$.

Space around an atomic nucleus contains the dimension 'to the power 4'. I had expected the Prime Number Cross to be somehow connected with matter. It is not only somehow connected with matter, each individual atom contains the information and structure of the prime number space. I was again shaken to the core by this discovery.

Conventional mathematics can be used to conduct a mechanical physics that describes things. In the 20th century, however, we began to discover something that could not be described free of contradictions without knowledge of four dimensions.

Mathematics had not given physicists a mathematical model with which they could even begin to examine four-dimensional space. The system of vector analysis of four-dimensional space that was available could not describe the various levels of reality but served only as a medium in which to conduct involved mental games.

Physicists therefore attempted to develop a single model of four-dimensionality, probably because they instinctively guessed that space really has four dimensions. But their model was doomed to failure from the very start since it is utter mathematical nonsense to try to link the three dimensions of space with one dimension of time.

I now knew at last why quantum mechanics had to fail. Although Neils Bohr proved back in 1913 that electrons move on specific paths at certain distances around the atomic nucleus, just like the planets around the sun, his model was originally rejected by the physicists. His postulates could not be reconciled with the accepted knowledge that electrons, unlike planets, have an electrical charge and therefore fall quickly into the nucleus (because of the opposing polarities of nucleus and electron cloud).

Bohr had conducted an ingenious examination of the distance between the electrons and the nucleus with the help of the reciprocal quadrate law. His postulate of the stable paths only found general acceptance when the general notion of the planetary electrons was discarded. The orbits of an electron are now described mathematically as a functional state and concepts such as probability of location have been introduced.

The contradiction inherent in atomic physics from the very beginning was never solved but only suppressed. The most whimsical arguments were supplied to cover up these inconsistencies. One of these is that the electrons remain on their stable paths because the (human-invented) 'laws of quantum mechanics tell them to do so' (C F von Weizäcker).

The real reasons are not known. This, however, does not prevent people from presenting modern physics as a comprehensively proven entity. Several generations of young people were deliberately misled. Whoever reads textbooks today will soon notice that almost everything is now being disputed, not only modern physics.

I explained my idea of the stationary path of the electron to Christina. **'Prime number space, which is arranged in the shape of shells and which surrounds every atomic nucleus, shifts the orbiting electrons at each point to the state $(-1)^4$. The exponent 'to the power 4' indicates the mathematical state of four-dimensional space. The electron has the charge -1. Because its state on the number shells of the space around the atomic nucleus is doubly squared, the minus sign is changed to a plus. In this way the electrons accept characteristics prescribed to them by the prime number space as four-dimensional space. They therefore have to follow the reciprocal quadrate law and can only occur on certain predetermined paths and in a certain quantity.'**

I now shifted the numbers -1, 0, $+1$ in figure 9 to the centre of the Prime Number Cross (figure 10). I gave this shell the name 'zero shell'. I did this, on the one hand, because it lies below the first shell and, on the other hand, because the numbers -1 and $+1$ produce in sum the value 0.

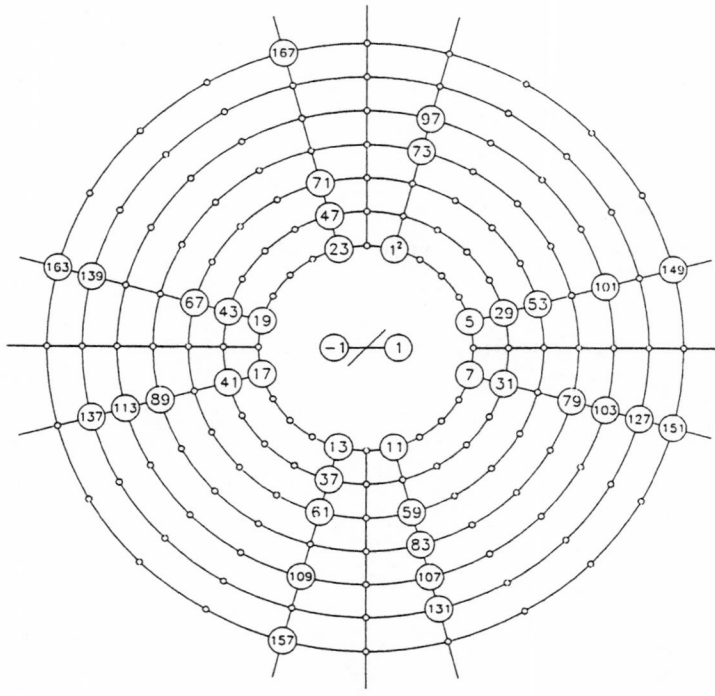

Figure 10

The number 0, that was 'discovered' in India, is the realization of one form of infinity – the infinitely small. Around this number which is not accessible to reason, Euler believed four root expressions of the number 1 to be located on a circle in the form of a cross. This is called the circle with radius.

Only a schematic indication of this circle with radius is given in figure 10, by a cross which from our perspective is slanted, and the numbers –1 and +1 (the axis for the root expressions of the number *i* are missing, as is the circle). Mathematicians have never felt the need to describe the space around the circle with radius, but this is exactly what is required here.[1]

The following numbers are then on the first circle:

$$0 \times 1^2, 1 \times 1^2, 2 \times 1^2, ..., 24 \times 1^2$$

The enlargement of the further numerical circles now takes place in the decimal system and leads to the other form of infinity – the infinitely large – which is as inaccessible to our

162

minds as the infinitely small.

An astonishingly close parallel to the Prime Number Cross which provides the construction plan for all matter occurs at one place in the New Testament book of Revelation. I present it here in an abbreviated form (in a translation from hitherto untranslated original texts prepared by the leading German rhetorician Walter Jens, Professor at the University of Tübingen).

It concerns God and the number of creatures that surround Him.

> In the centre was the One, the unnameable, surrounded by four powerful beings. And around the throne were the 24 chairs with the 24 elders. They prayed to the unnameable: Through you alone all things and all beings exist. Your will enabled them to be and gave them form. Around the throne, around the four powerful beings, and around the elders there were 10,000 times 10,000 and again 1,000 times and again 1,000 angels.

There was a time I used to make fun of the Apocalypse of St John and believed it to be a totally unreliable historical source. Today I am filled with deep humility, perhaps because I am now able to give a concrete description of the foundation of the world as seen by St John with my mathematical discoveries, and thus possibly open a new way to all of humanity which has now reached a dead end.

The constant of numeric expansion had to be increased by the factor 1^2 in 1986 and now has the value

$$3 \times 1^2 \times 10^2 \times 100^2 \times 1,000^2 \ldots$$

The formula shows how elegantly numerical space can be linked with the decimal system. Because every expansion in space is linked to time in our human understanding, we automatically link the expansion of light to the notion of speed.

It is known that Einstein even as a young man considered whether it would be possible to fly after a beam of light. He later managed to consider existing formulas of physics from a different perspective and was thus able to create his theories of relativity. The theories exclude the possibility of any body being accelerated to the 'speed' of light. The impossibility of this feat is proved by the formula that appears in thousands of textbooks which shows that the mass of a body would increase towards infinity at such an acceleration, and this is clearly not possible. Our age therefore now has an idea of relativity which finds more popular admiration than any other theory, and which – because of the contradictions it contains – is also fanatically contested. But for various reasons, neither side is interested in discovering the real background to the question. I therefore decided at that time to keep the solution of the problem to myself. I also felt that I would uncover even more dramatic contradictions.

Because the Prime Number Cross is constructed from three base numbers and describes four-dimensional space around every point (every atomic nucleus), the 3^4 law must consequently be incorporated in the chemical elements themselves. The reciprocal value of the number 81 provides the decimal numerical sequence, written without a decimal point,

$$0\ 0\ 1\ 2\ 3\ 4\ 5\ \dots$$

The elements of the Periodic Table are ordered in this sequence. Scientists will object that the sequence of the ordered decimal numbers only begins after the decimal point and thus each subsequent number must first be divided by 10, 100, 1,000 (0 divided by 10, 1 divided by 100, 2 divided by 1,000, etc.).

In order to defuse this argument, I searched for a further possibility of finding this numerical sequence (if necessary without a decimal point). I again became intensively involved with the primary numbers of the type $6n \pm 1$ and their multiples:

$$(-1;1),\ (5;7),\ (11;13),\ (17;19),\ (23;25),\ (29;31),\ \dots$$

The elements of each pair differ by 2 and the elements themselves are separated by 4.

I was suddenly mesmerized and stared at the ray on the Prime Number Cross on which the square numbers of all prime numbers of the form $6n \pm 1$ are located (figure 8, page 156, in which the 1 $[= (-1^2)]$ below the 1^2 on the zero shell is not yet indicated). I had finally found what I had been looking for!

$(-1)^2\_1^2$, $5^2\_7^2$, 73, 97, 11^2, 145, 13^2, 193, 217, 241, 265, 17^2, 313, 337, 19^2, 385, 409, 433, 457, 481, 505, 23^2, 553, 577, 601, 25^2, 649, 673, 697, 721, 745, 769, 793, 817, 29^2,

865, 889, 913, 937, **31²**, 985, 1009, 1033, 1057, 1081, 1105, 1129, 1153, 1177, 1201, **35²**, 1249, 1273, 1297, 1321, 1345, **37²**, ...

No number occurs between the squares of the first twins $(-1)^2$ and 1^2. I marked in a zero. The same applies to the squares of the second twins, 5^2 and 7^2, so I again put in a zero. Between 11^2 and 13^2 the first 'filler' number occurs, 145. I put in a one. Between the next squares 5^2 and 7^2, two filler numbers appear – 313 and 337. This is followed by three filler numbers, then four, five, and so on. I noted the sequence of numbers

$$0\ 0\ 1\ 2\ 3\ 4\ 5\ ...$$

The small and familiar comma does not occur here (thank God!).

The search for the 3^4 law on the Prime Number Cross thus turned out to be the dissolution of the reciprocal square law in the decimal system. The difference of 2 between the first four prime number twins gives us in the linear sequence

$$0\ 1\ 2\ 3\ 4\ 5\ ...$$

and in the quadratic the decimal sequence

$$0\ 0\ 1\ 2\ 3\ 4\ 5\ ...$$

This means that the quadrature of the linear sequence of numbers again shows an order. But it is not the order of square numbers, it is a decimal order.

This augurs a revolution for our primary schools. Nothing less than the atomic model and the chemical elements themselves will in future be their godfathers when children develop a relationship to numbers. Our children have the opportunity of being the first generation to be able to fully appreciate the meaning in at least one Bible quotation –

> But THOU hast arranged all things by measure and number and weight.
>
> Wisdom 11:20

My suspicion had now become certainty. If space expands according to the decimal system, then the material that fills this space must also be structured according to this system. And that is exactly the way it is. The chemical elements are constructed according to the order of the natural numbers. At the same time each and every element must have a specific number of isotopes, a number between 0 and 10.

My work in the field of theoretical physics and chemistry had now come to an end for the time being. I would now have to devote some years entirely to mathematics.

The history of the natural sciences is characterized by errors, whereas the only errors mathematics will admit to are errors in calculation. With regard to errors, mathematicians believe they are infallible, for all theorems can be logically proved.

Moreover, mathematicians have never asked the question why. Because numbers are, at least according to scientific opinion, a purely human invention, clever proofs of nothing but imaginative guesswork are considered an expression of the mathematical intelligence of the problem-solver.

But if this world is a self-realization of the infinity of space-time and numbers, and can only be arranged in mathematical structures, there must be a certain – perhaps common – background to the proven mathematical theorems. There must be an answer to the question why these laws really exist.

I therefore investigated various mathematical theorems and became more and more astonished at how blind not only the mathematical elite has been, but also how superficially I myself had passed over the true connections.

I would like to illustrate this fascinating notion with two of the most famous theorems in mathematics – the principle of transcendence in the numbers e and π (C Hermite and F von Lindemann), and the prime number principle (J Hadamard and C de la Vallée Poussin). Both laws are found in mathematics isolated alongside each other. I began to suspect that there was a correlation between these and other laws.

The proofs are considered so difficult to comprehend that they are even excluded from normal mathematics, although ordinary swotting by students would in any case hardly lead to major leaps forward.

But this is precisely why the mathematics student is prevented from investigating why these two theorems exist at all in the world.

166

I shall try to make the depth and significance of this enquiry and its solution familiar to the reader who is not versed in mathematics.

In mathematics a distinction is made between three different types in decimal fractions with an infinite number of places after the decimal point.

Recurring decimal fractions are rational. Root expressions may be irrational if they are not precise decimal fractions and if they do not partly or wholly recur. Infinite decimal fractions, which can be categorized neither in the first nor in the second group, cannot be conceptualized other than in approximations by us and are therefore called transcendental.

This division into the three types – **rational**, **irrational**, and **transcendental** – of decimal numbers has led to the question of which group the numbers e and π should be categorized within.

Archimedes studied π. He wanted to find out what fraction was closest to its value. The approximate value of $3\frac{1}{7}$ which he discovered is still used today in our schools in the form of the fraction 22/7. In post-Renaissance mathematics, everything was geared towards finding two numbers which as a fraction approaching infinity could produce exactly π. In 1770 the question was finally answered in the negative. Mathematicians then concentrated on the question of whether π could be worked out through root expressions. If this was not the case, then π had to be a transcendental number – and this reasoning brings us to the very centre of the most profound mathematical enquiries.

The mysterious, infinite decimal numbers e and π can be linked to each other by an extremely curious formula. The formula was discovered by Euler and reads:

$$e^{i\pi} = -1$$

Euler was very enthusiastic about his discovery, although his contemporaries considered it just a mathematical conceit.

Carl Gauss, who as a schoolboy had studied Euler's mathematical writings, elevated this so that it became the central formula of mathematics. Because it is relatively simple to deduce this formula today, most mathematicians no longer consider it mysterious. Every electronic calculator in any secondary school can work out what $e = 2.718$ ... to the power of 3.141 produces (to as many places as it can calculate). However, no computer in the world can work out this value when the number i (the root of -1) occurs in the power.

The proof of the transcendence of π was provided by the above Euler formula, when the proof had been provided beforehand that e is transcendental (and not algebraic). And if the expression $i \times \pi$ is transcendental (and not algebraic), then π must also be transcendental.

The proof that e is also a transcendental number was undertaken by the use of a premise which led to a contradiction in the course of the proof. The premise must therefore be false. (Mathematicians use this method to develop proofs which are not directly provable.)

Although this proof was ingenious, it contained absolutely nothing to explain **why the basic constants of the universe are transcendental.**

Now back to the prime number law. It has its origins in the belief that the number of prime numbers below a certain number obeys certain laws. If you want to know whether 101 is a prime number, it is quite possible to try to factorize the number in your head. You will then find that it is indivisible and therefore a prime number. With the number 1,000,001, the necessary calculation is considerably more difficult. If there is no formula to establish whether a number is a prime number or not, it would seem at least important to know whether there is a formula for the number of prime numbers. Between the numbers 1 and 1,000,000 there are no fewer than 78,496 prime numbers, which can only be calculated by painstaking counting through tables.

Whoever has a suitable calculator can easily enter the number 1,000,000 and then press the button that designates the natural logarithm to the base e. The calculator will give the value 13.8 ... . The 15-year-old Gauss, who had access to a table of prime numbers and logarithms, now hit on the idea of dividing the number 1,000,000 by the value 13.8 and got an answer that rounded up to 72,463. If this number is compared with the number of prime numbers above, 78,496, it will be seen that they are separated only by about 6,000.

Gauss now suspected that the number of prime numbers

below a certain number would always obey the formula 'x divided by the natural logarithm of x' as the numbers forever increased upwards (eg one thousand million, a billion, a trillion, a quadrillion, and so on) As a young boy he had discovered a formula that was even more precise, called the integral logarithm, but until the end of his life he was not able to find the general proof. One of his successors, Bernd Riemann, again found a more precise formula but was still unable to provide the general proof.

It was not until 1896 that Hadamard and his colleague Poussin proved independently of each other that *in infinite dimensions the number of prime numbers is (asymptotically) equal to*

$$\frac{x}{\text{natural logarithm } x}$$

Hadamard was born in 1865 and lived for almost 100 years. He was one of the greatest mathematicians of all time and laid the foundation for the solution of the 'riddle of the universe'. But as a mathematician he was blind to this knowledge and 'only' searched for a formula.

It should have been clear that the prime numbers are strictly linked to the natural logarithm, and thus with the basic constant of the universe, the number e. It is all the more astonishing that Hadamard did not go on to establish this, since he also published significant mathematical work in physics.

It was already well known then that absolutely no description of physical phenomena can be made without the natural logarithm, so Hadamard should really have suspected a correlation between physical processes and the distribution of the prime numbers. The fact that the formula to calculate the number of prime numbers does not produce the precise number of prime numbers – as shown above – probably contributed considerably to this mental block.[2]

In order to clear up the mistakes made by mathematicians in the past thoroughly and quickly, I needed the support of an excellent young specialist mathematician (still capable of enthusiasm). And once again my wish was fulfilled.

In December 1987 I met a young mathematician at a friend's birthday party. He soon moved into my house for some months to take lessons from me. Michael Felton was 23 years old and was preparing for his Master's degree.

He was the fourth child of a gardener. His parents never noticed the mathematical talents of the young boy, and he was not sent to a secondary school but generally put to looking after the garden. Then, just as in the case of Gauss, a teacher at his school recognized the boy's ability and made sure that he was immediately transferred to one of the upper grades of the local secondary school.

He passed his undergraduate tests with As, and in his main thesis he was the first exam candidate of the mathematical institute of the University of Dortmund ever to complete all three mathematical subjects with the highest grade of A+.

Drawn to mathematics by a deep love for the subject, he immediately realized that he would urgently have to study the original writings of the great mathematicians in addition to the secondary literature familiar to him from the university. He was also able to catch up on the gaps in his knowledge of the history of mathematics very quickly. In addition to this, he received private tutoring from me in the subjects of chemistry, physics and biology.

We could now begin.

At that time the Atari ST 1024 computer with a hard disk had just come onto the market and was a godsend to us. With this machine, mathematical publications could be properly and conveniently written for the first time. Michael and I began, in addition to our research work, to type into the computer the manuscript of my book *The Prime Number Cross*, which had so far only been produced on the typewriter. Typing had been a very tiring task, partly because of the many mathematical formulas, tables and diagrams.

Parallel to this work on the book, Christina and I forced ourselves to plough through the difficult philosophical work *The Critique of Pure Reason* by Immanuel Kant. Both of us had previously made several vain attempts to come to grips with his words.

While we were occupied with Kant, who is probably the one philosopher to have devoted most of his energy to space and time, I began to understand that two types of space must really exist. On the one hand the three-dimensional space of our daily world in which atoms, molecules and, in fact, all objects occur (objective space) and, on the other hand, the infinite space around every object (subjective space).

Our research in these areas, which had to be constantly subject to revision and monitoring, was often punctuated by necessary telephone conversations with Michael, who lived on and off in Dortmund. To facilitate quick and easy communication between us, we had adopted many neologisms in addition to normal mathematical jargon. The result could not have been in greater contrast to the language of Kant. If anybody had heard us, he or she would have been quite stupefied.

NOTES

1 For mathematicians: to go from i to -1, a turn of 90° must be made, from -1 to $+1$ a turn of 180° is necessary. When the circle with radius is left a 360° turn must therefore be made and a new circle introduced. The polar co-ordinant presentation is: $e^{4\pi i} = 1^2$.

2 Hadamard writes (translated from the French): 'My intention was to show that zeta from s can have no zero places of which the real part equals 1.' A reader versed in mathematics will recognize that a statement is made here about the infinite path of a graphic curve depicting complex numbers (a curve on which all prime numbers are found).

171

CHAPTER FIFTEEN

THE ORDER WITHIN DISORDER

The number e (= 2.718 ...) was developed by Newton from a factorial series in 1665. He immediately recognized the importance of the number and was able to prove its significance with mathematical rigour. The algebraic letter e was, however, only introduced by Euler in 1739. He found a second possibility, entirely different from the first, of differentiating the number e and also of proving it. This was done by binomials.

The possibility of differentiating this mysterious number in two totally different ways appeared extremely puzzling to me. Michael and I had agreed that the double differentiation through factorials and binomials must be an indication that the number e, which is the basic constant of the universe, must have something to do with the order and combination of the number sequence.[1]

'Michael, if our Prime Number Cross is the foundation of the order of this world, the reason for the differentiation of e from the series of factorials must lie in the cyclical structure of the prime numbers.'

Michael clenched his fist and shouted, 'Peter, we are going to get to the bottom of this! I feel I know the solution already.'

'Michael, I believe that if we want to solve this profound riddle, we shall have to keep our eyes on the zero shell.'

And we did keep our eyes on it.

The value 1.718 ... is calculated according to Newton as follows:

$$\frac{1}{1} + \frac{1}{1 \times 2} + \frac{1}{1 \times 2 \times 3} + \frac{1}{1 \times 2 \times 3 \times 4} + \cdots = \frac{1}{1!} + \frac{1}{2!} + \frac{1}{3!} + \frac{1}{4!} + \cdots$$

$$= 1.718 \ldots$$

The missing 1 (from $e = 2.718 \ldots$) was provided by Newton by continuing his factorial series for one more function, namely

$$\frac{1}{0!}$$

He reckoned this expression to equal 1, compensating for the dubious nature of this procedure by the proof that e must have the value 2.718 ....

In the spring of 1989 we again removed the questionable expression 1/0! from the formula. What remained was the numerical value 1.718 ....

We attempted to reach the value 1.718 in a comprehensible way. We developed a combination game with different numbers of balls. If only one ball marked 1 is in a box, we only have one possibility of taking out this ball and placing it in front of us. If two balls marked 1 and 2 are in the box, we have two possibilities of taking them out and lining them up in a certain order (1; 2) (2; 1). With three balls we have six possibilities (1; 2; 3), (1; 3; 2), (2; 1; 3), (2; 3; 1), (3; 1; 2) and (3 ;2; 1); with four balls we have 24, with 5 balls 120 possibilities, and so on.

In order to obtain a numerical series with the order of the sequential numbers, with one number there is only one possibility for the number 1. With two numbers the chance of the correct order is one of two possibilities. With three numbers the chance is one of six; and with four numbers it is one of 24 possibilities. The result gives the following illustration of the chances of sequential numerical series: first with one ball, then with two, three and four balls, etc:

$$\frac{1}{1} + \frac{1}{2} + \frac{1}{6} + \frac{1}{24} + \cdots$$

The sum of the combinations when we continue this game indefinitely amounts to

$$1.718 \ldots$$

The Newtonian factorial series thus turns out to be pure

173

combination analysis for numerical sequences. Newton was certainly aware of this, but with his notorious secrecy he kept it to himself that the value of $e - 1 = 1.718$ comes from nothing other than the order of the natural numbers themselves. The missing 1, however, did not fit into this wonderful concept.

So where should we now get this 1 from? At the same moment both of us suddenly remembered my warning that we should keep our eyes on the zero shell, because this contains only one order – ie 1 (and its root expressions). I can graphically recall the moment our thoughts crossed and the connection was clearly seen. We now had it – the number e derived from the Prime Number Cross. As long as this model of reality was not available for numbers positioned in order on circles, the logic of mathematics had always to be in direct contradiction to the reality of the world. Mathematicians consider e to be a great human achievement – an abstract, invented unit. The fact that it is also coincidentally the basic constant of the universe is registered with overweening vanity.

It was now clear that the mathematical constant e was related to the structure and distribution of the prime numbers of the form $6n \pm e$. At the same time we had the solution to the problem of why the three mathematical constants e, i, and π are linked with the number -1 through the formula $e^{i\pi} = -1$.

Because $-1 + 1 = 0$, we have the result (when $+1$ is added to both sides): $e^{i\pi} + 1 = 0.$

This formula contains the six basic units of mathematics

$$e, i, \pi, 1, 0, -1.$$

We were able to decipher this fundamental mathematical secret because only the Prime Number Cross offers the possibility of illustrating these six basic units of the universe. π is the number used in calculating circles and it repeats itself in all numerical circles. The imaginary number i determines the cross structure of the zero shell. The number e provides the order for the successive numbers, although the only thing that is important here is the structure and distribution of the prime numbers.

The Prime Number Cross is thus not a human invention. It is in fact a model of the construction plan with which infinity was made finite in the structure of atoms. It is therefore also the case that we are not inventors in this field. We were looking for something and we found it. This also means that the Prime Number Cross is impervious to any human derogatory judgements.

Whoever wants to really understand these connections will understand them and be filled with awe. God arranged the world simply. He certainly did not intend that comprehension of His world would be restricted to elite groups in universities. It was humankind itself which took the infinite plurality of the cosmos and created an insurmountable complexity of formulas. But whoever wants to emerge from the captivity of contemporary knowledge, irrespective of the reason, will have to bear the consequences.

Truth does not need people to understand it, but people need truth in order to really live.

With the discovery of differential and integral calculus by Leibniz and Newton three hundred years ago, mathematics reached a stage which we now refer to as higher mathematics. Michael and I guessed that all higher mathematics with its enormous variety and complexity must actually be nothing less than a veneer over the prime numbers.

Michael got his master's degree in the summer of 1989 and meant to write his PhD over the following two years. But first he allowed the subject which he had chosen as his doctoral thesis to rest for two years. The problem that he wanted to investigate had in any case remained unsolved for about one hundred years, before he finally solved it in six months in 1991.

By then we had managed to uncover the hidden secrets of higher mathematics with such intricate skill as if we had managed to break into the safes of the Bank of England and got away with the loot. Our elation could be seen in our faces.

The story of this unravelling began in September 1989 on Königsallee, the main boulevard of Düsseldorf. We sat in the sun outside a street café and ate plum cake with a double portion of cream. Our conversation revolved, as always, around prime numbers. Suddenly I hit on an elementary connection.

'Michael, the numbers +1 and −1 are the basic numbers from which the prime numbers of the form $6n \pm 1$ are derived. Leibniz was the first to realize that calculus is in principle based on these two numbers. For integration +1 is added to the exponent to calculate a surface section below a curve to an infinite degree of precision. For differentiation, the number −1 is added to the exponent to determine the curvature of a line to an infinite degree of precision. Because ±1 is the rhythm of the prime numbers, integral and differential calculus must be connected to the prime numbers (in exponential series).'

Michael sat there with his mouth open: 'Good grief, have we been stupid? You are right, Peter. No mathematician has expressed this idea for three hundred years. The prime numbers are linked to the natural logarithm and this is in turn related to integral calculus. Integral calculus[2] must therefore be connected in some way with prime numbers. That's so obvious that I feel I'm going crazy.'

I asked a question which only occurred to me at that moment: 'Michael, so far we've only occupied ourselves with whole numbers on circles. If the numbers exist in reality, their reciprocal values must also exist in the real world. But where do they actually lie on the Prime Number Cross?'

Michael looked at me in surprise. He thought for a while and said; 'They will not be between the numbers zero and 1 on the Prime Number Cross at any rate.'

The whole numbers on the Prime Number Cross are always located on four different segments (quadrants) of the circle. If we can imagine the reverse of the whole numbers, we should also be able to imagine the inversion of the segments of a circle.

And that is indeed how it was. At the end of 1989 I was able to dissolve the mental block. Geometrically speaking, reciprocal numbers are located on a curve called a hyperbola. We define this curve as the inversion of infinitely small sections of increasingly large circles. Mathematicians are not generally aware of this relation to the circles.

The reciprocal value of 1 is 1/1, the reciprocal value of 2 is 1/2, the reciprocal value of 3 is 1/3, etc. Figure 11 shows a hyperbolic branch that approaches the x-axis on the right side but can never reach it. The infinity of the whole numbers is to be found with the reciprocal value on the y-axis between 1 and 0. The number 0 can, however, never be reached.

Our studies of the hyperbola again brought us back to the natural logarithm and to the prime numbers.

We want to start with the question of how big – for example

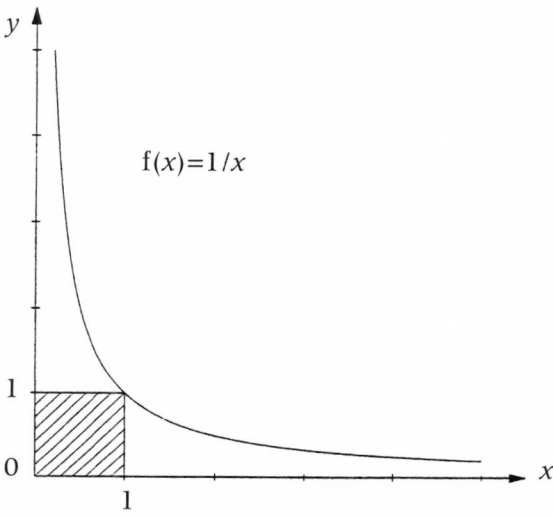

Figure 11

– the sum of the first million reciprocal numbers is:

$$1 + \frac{1}{2} + \frac{1}{3} + \frac{1}{4} + \frac{1}{5} + \frac{1}{6} + \frac{1}{7} + \ldots + \frac{1}{1,000,000}$$

Most people probably think that it is necessary to go to all the trouble of converting these fractions to decimal and then adding them.

$$1 + 0.5 + 0.3333 \ldots + 0.25 + 0.1666 \ldots + 0.142857 \ldots$$
$$\text{etc.}$$

But just as with the question of the number of prime numbers below a million, the pocket calculator again helps us to make a rapid calculation in this case. We again simply enter the value 1,000,000 and press the natural logarithm button. The familiar value 13.81 ... then appears, which differs from the true value 14.39 ... of the added reciprocal numbers by a decimal fraction which is referred to as (capital) C and measures

$$0.5772156649 \ldots$$

This number is known as the Euler-Mascheroni constant. The value of this constant occurs more and more precisely if we continue the addition towards infinity. The capital C is a

177

mathematical constant, just like the Euler number e. Otherwise nothing is known about C. We do not even know if it is a transcendental number, as e is.

It is, of course, strange that the natural logarithm (which is linked to the number e) provides the approximate number of prime numbers and also the result for the sum of reciprocal numbers. The number of prime numbers is apparently connected with the sum of the reciprocal numbers.

So far we have not explained what it is precisely that links e to the natural logarithm. Any interested reader can look this up in a mathematical textbook. It is enough to know here that the number e and the natural logarithm are linked together by an inverse relation which is, however, not so simple as the relation between a number and its reciprocal value.

If the reciprocal values are linked to e and/or the natural logarithm, and e in its turn is related to the order of the prime numbers, the order of the prime numbers must be related to the order of the reciprocal numbers.

Because the Prime Number Cross with the sequence of the whole numbers contains a certain geometry that is indicated by the base numbers 1, 2 and 3 and the eight-ray structure, the order of the reciprocal numbers – we deduced almost in a fever – must also have a (reciprocal) geometry which would have to be based on the numbers 1, 2, 3 and a multiple eight structure.

I had now again returned to the question whether two spaces had to exist at the same time – space around an object (infinite and four-dimensional) and the space in which the object is observed (finite and three-dimensional). This three-dimensional space, in which we 'live' is generally filled with gas. In this gas mixture, there are transport operations that are so common that we scarcely think about them. These include the transmission of sound and language (acoustics) and transmission of heat (thermodynamics). Because our notion of space has so far always been fixed on three-dimensional space, it has not been possible for scientists to even imagine four-dimensional (numerical) space. The point is that three-dimensional space can only be appreciated as numerical space of the reciprocal numbers when the space of the whole numbers, four-dimensional space, has been comprehended.

When we pluck a note on the string of a violin, the string

begins to vibrate and the note is carried by the air to our ears. This is a curious phenomenon. The gas molecules collide with each other in the same way as billiard balls. The number of molecules in a litre of gas is unimaginably high (approximately 10^{22}). When an entire orchestra plays in a hall, the confusion that then reigns in the molecules of the air is so enormous that every explanation to date for explaining sound transmission is inadequate. The music that reaches us from the stage and is reflected a thousand-fold on walls, ceiling, rows of seats, etc. should really hit our ears as an unbearable screeching. Instead infinitely precise information reaches our eardrums, whether as vibrations or through the medium of electrical signals.

Just as light passes through empty or gas-filled space in waves (although the gas does not function as a medium in this case), so also is sound physically transmitted through a gas-filled space, whereby the colliding gas molecules are alternately compressed and attenuated in the gas medium. These transporting phenomena are referred to as longitudinal waves. Although they are able to indicate the speed of sound as a wave occurrence, they give no explanation of the precise transmission of information.

In modern physics there are two wave models. The electromagnetic transverse waves run through empty space. The longitudinal (sound) wave is transported precisely by a gas medium and thus carries information of an incredible range. Both should be considered magical by physicists in that they have no viable explanation for these phenomena. But magic has no place in physics. Physicists work with laws that are handed down to them and they are vain enough to believe they have created these laws.

When a chemist brings two or more materials in a solution to boil, he has succeeded either in making the molecules collide violently with each other and thus form compounds according to certain reaction mechanisms, or in causing transformations in the molecules themselves. When, on the other hand, we think of a single cell in a leaf or of the liver cell in an animal, our ability to imagine the collision processes (kinetics) fails.

The incredible chaos involving multiple collisions of thousands of different chemical compounds which are all split into specific 'billiard balls' is in complete contradiction to the

179

observed order of all processes. It is true that spatially constructed enzymes cause production processes similar to the conveyor belts in automobile assembly, but the real order in chaos is nevertheless completely incomprehensible.

In recent years a new trend has developed in modern physics called chaos theory. Again only the phenomena that are observed are described, unfortunately. There is no attempt to discover who or what controls the 'order' in chaos. This line of enquiry was now of immediate concern to me.

Because transverse electromagnetic waves are transported through the prime number structure of four-dimensional space with infinite precision, the transport mechanism for the collision processes in three-dimensional space could only be caused by the sequence of the reciprocal prime numbers.

Collision processes are dual decisions and we would like to give a brief mathematical illustration of the left-or-right decision, the classical dualism between yes or no, heads or tails. For this we require a board of nails, the so-called Galton board. This is fitted with a funnel at the top; in the middle there is an apex triangle formation of nails; and at the bottom there is a row of more narrow boxes, open at the top. If small balls are now dropped into the funnel from the top, they will hit against the nails in a regular fashion as they fall down and will thus be knocked to each side.

The balls then lie in a certain distribution in the collecting boxes. Instead of using a nail board, we can empty a sack of rice from a chosen height onto the ground. This will produce very

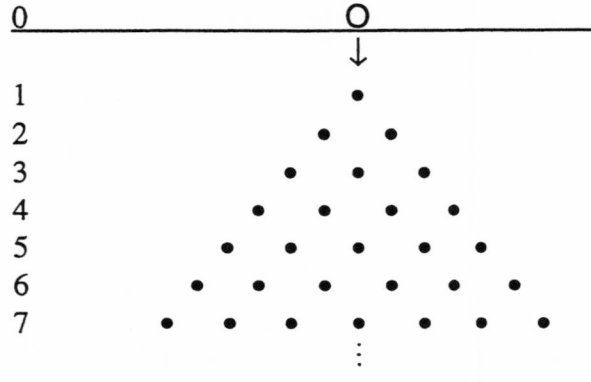

Figure 12

180

much the same picture. The pile will be biggest in the centre and will gradually level out towards the edges. If this resulting form is drawn into a curve, the result will be the so-called Gauss distribution curve. This curve repeats itself again and again in distribution operations. It is also linked to the number e, which is only to be expected. How do the grains of rice know that they have to obey a natural constant?

The question is: how can an experimental order consisting of purely binary decisions lead to a distribution that conforms to the natural constant e. A ball must only 'decide' each time it hits a nail whether it will fall to the left or to the right. The decision for the left or the right presents two possible events. We can therefore formulate the question: How is the number 2 related to the natural constant e?

The decision whether a ball will fall to the right or to the left is purely a spatial problem. Knowledge of the prime numbers will not directly help us further in this case. But the suspicion has been aroused that apart from the universality of the numbers 3 and 4, as well as 1, the number 2 will also be assigned a deeper, as yet undiscovered fundamental meaning. It is the number of the decision, the number of so-called chance chains.

To help us examine the statistics of a two-body collision, we can consider the path of a single ball falling down through a board of nails. The ball should fall from the zero level and has only one possibility of direction of fall. If it falls onto the first nail, it can be deflected in its fall to the right or to the left. The probability that it falls to the right is $\frac{1}{2}$. On falling to the second level the ball again has the 'choice' to fall to the right or to the left. If it again falls to the right, the probability is $\frac{1}{2} \times \frac{1}{2}$. On the third level, the value for the decision to fall to the right is now $\frac{1}{2} \times \frac{1}{2} \times \frac{1}{2}$, etc. We then add each separate rate of probability for the continued infinite fall to the right and obtain

$$1 + \frac{1}{2} + \frac{1}{4} + \frac{1}{8} + \ldots = 2$$

We should now consider the descent of the ball when there is a free choice.

The descent of the ball from the zero to the first level is the same as in the above example. At the second level there is 1 way

181

$$
\begin{array}{ccccccccc}
 & & & & 1 & & & & & \rightarrow & 1 = 2^0 \\
 & & & 1 & & 1 & & & & \rightarrow & 2 = 2^1 \\
 & & 1 & & 2 & & 1 & & & \rightarrow & 4 = 2^2 \\
 & 1 & & 3 & & 3 & & 1 & & \rightarrow & 8 = 2^3 \\
1 & & 4 & & 6 & & 4 & & 1 & \rightarrow & 16 = 2^4 \\
\end{array}
$$

1   5 10 10 5 1   → $32 = 2^5$

1 6 15 20 15 6 1   → $64 = 2^6$

1 7 21 35 35 21 7 1 → $128 = 2^7$

1 8 28 56 70 56 28 8 1 → $256 = 2^8$

⋮

Figure 13

leading to the left nail and 1 way to the right nail. To the middle nail in the third level there are then exactly 2 ways. Each of the two middle nails in the fourth level can be reached by 3 ways. At the next level there are combinations of 1, 4, 6, 4, 1 possible ways to reach each nail.

These numbers of combination are called binomial co-efficients (a real tongue-twister). In the course of what follows, I shall reveal their fascinating secret.

In general, we obtain the above pattern – which is called Pascal's Triangle after the French mathematician and philosopher Blaise Pascal.

The rule for each level is: the sum of the possibilities of paths is always a power of the number 2. With a falling ball, one possibility is chosen at each level from the sum of all combinations – ie from 2^n,

$$\frac{1}{2^n}$$

The comparison with the reciprocal square law is amazing. It can be seen at a glance that the base numbers and the exponents (2 and n) have only been exchanged. This is a result of the fact described below that the lines of Pascal's Triangle must be described with reciprocal numbers.

The two laws

$$\frac{1}{2^n} \text{ and } \frac{1}{n^2}$$

describe, as we shall see in the next chapter the mutually

reciprocal geometries of three-dimensional and four-dimensional space.

From the addition of the reciprocal value of the numbers 1, 2, 4, 8, 16, 32, ... we obtain the value 2. This number must be a natural constant. There is good reason to believe that the number 2 and the natural constant e are closely related, for both of them were obtained from a related order concept.

But what connects the numbers 2 and e? When a number of balls run through the board, the distribution is in the form of a bell curve. The precision increases with the number of levels and balls (Gauss distribution curve e^{-x^2}). In this way we can directly reach the heart of the matter. We now conduct an imaginary experiment.

Again we have the balls. However, this time we do not take one marked ball from the box, but empty the whole box of unmarked balls through the nail board. Whereas in the first game we reached the number e by adding all chances in the ordered series, we would now like to leave it to chance and discover if any order is obtained.

At the zero level a ball has only one possibility of direction of fall. It should fall onto the first nail (first level). Whether it now falls to the right will be decisive for its final position in the distribution curve. The position of its decision on the second curve therefore depends on the decision at the level above. This also applies to the nail which the ball hits at the third level. This is again dependent on the procedure at the level above. It can therefore be deduced that the importance of the individual levels becomes reduced as we go down.

The nth level has n nails. The importance of the individual levels for the final position of the ball therefore runs through the reciprocal numbers

$$1, \frac{1}{2}, \frac{1}{3}, \frac{1}{4}, \frac{1}{5}, \ldots$$

The probability of the ball's direction of fall to the left or to the right is 1/2 in each case. A ball should now ideally fall alternately to the left and the right. It would then fall directly in the middle of the Gauss bell curve. The importance of the levels through which it falls also decreases as described above. The alternating direction of fall to the left or to the right is now replaced by a change in sign of plus and minus in the total. The result is the 'Mercator series', so called after the cartographer Mercator:

$$1 - \frac{1}{2} + \frac{1}{3} - \frac{1}{4} + \frac{1}{5} - + \ldots = 0.69314 \ldots = \text{natural logarithm 2}$$

If an infinite number of balls were to run through an infinite number of levels, the distribution of the balls would be exactly symmetrical because the left-decision and the right-decision are equally probable. The value for the aforementioned zigzag path in the middle of the nail board is 0.69314 ....

This is the natural logarithm of a whole number to the base e. It is the logarithm of the number 2 which steers the yes-no decision.

$$e^{0.69314\ldots} = 2$$

So, whereas our first game led to the natural constant e, the ordered zigzag process in the form of balls falling 'by chance' gave us the natural logarithm of the number 2. The frequency curve has its apex in the centre of the nail board. The distribution curve can thus only be an e function if the events on the nail board are mathematically linked to the natural logarithm.

Because the importance of the levels must be described with reciprocal numbers, it is clear that the lines in Pascal's Triangle must also generally be described with reciprocal numbers and that the logarithm must be steered through the order of the reciprocal prime numbers – as will be made clear in the next chapter.

The nail board is only a model to illustrate the yes-no decisions. For an amount of gas atoms which collide with each other, the same mathematical law applies as in the case of the nail board model. The collisions of the individual atoms with each other (two-body collisions) appear to us to be entirely random. But for an increasing number of collisions the entire system becomes increasingly more ordered. It must be described mathematically with e functions or the reverse, the natural logarithm.

We obtained the natural logarithm of 2 from the alternating series addition of the reciprocal numbers. The alternating series

$$+, -, +, -, +, -, +. \ldots$$

is a statistical representation of an order, an *order within disorder*, for there are infinitely many plus-minus series that are not alternating and are thus random.

We finally began to understand that three-dimensional gas-filled space is a reciprocal numerical space. It must be ordered by reciprocal prime numbers and be a geometric realization of the reversal of four-dimensional, empty, infinite space as ordered by prime numbers in the Prime Number Cross.

NOTES

1 Every student today can go from the differentiation of the logarithm function to the binomial $(1 + \frac{1}{n})^n$ with the greatest of ease and transfer this binomial by introducing a limiting value into the factorial series: $1 + \frac{1}{1!} + \frac{1}{2!} + \frac{1}{3!} + \frac{1}{4!} + \ldots$ All amazement at the two different ways of calculating e has accordingly disappeared.

2 The integral of $1/x$ according to the integration method of Leibniz results in a contradiction – the undefined expression '1 divided by 0'.

$$\int \frac{1}{x} dx = \frac{x^{-1+1}}{-1+1} = \frac{x^0}{0} = \frac{1}{0}$$

Three hundred years ago, Liebniz's critics were euphoric, but only until it turned out that this integral contains a reasonable solution, ie (natural logarithm) x. Because the mathematical step of integrating $1/x$ is the most frequently used mathematical operation in physics, one can only shake one's head at the thoughtlessness with which natural logarithms are treated in this science.

185

CHAPTER SIXTEEN

THE SEARCH FOR RECIPROCAL GEOMETRY

The numbers in Pascal's Triangle are calculated from binomials of the type $(a+b)^n$. Almost all of us will vaguely remember a formula we had to learn off by heart at school: 'a plus b in brackets squared equals a squared plus $2ab$ plus b squared'. This can be seen in the third line in figure 14.

$$(a+b)^0 = \mathbf{1}$$
$$(a+b)^1 = \mathbf{1}a + \mathbf{1}b$$
$$(a+b)^2 = \mathbf{1}a^2 + \mathbf{2}ab + \mathbf{1}b^2$$
$$(a+b)^3 = \mathbf{1}a^3 + \mathbf{3}a^2b + \mathbf{3}b^2a + \mathbf{1}b^3$$
$$(a+b)^4 = \mathbf{1}a^4 + \mathbf{4}a^3b + \mathbf{6}a^2b^2 + \mathbf{4}b^3a + \mathbf{1}b^4$$
$$\vdots$$

Figure 14

The special thing about binomial coefficients is that it is not necessary to multiply them out according to the above complicated process – they are simply the result of addition (see figure 13, page 182). The two ones in the second line are added to give the two in the next line below, and the one and two of the third line add to give the three in the fourth line. The sum of the two threes in the fourth line provides the number six in the fifth line. This puzzling order becomes even more mysterious when it is discovered in the eighth line that all numbers of the line, apart from the two ones at the sides, are divisible by the two coefficients, the prime number 7.

1, 7, 21, 35, 35, 21, 7, 1

The rule can be stated generally: 'When the exponent of the binomial is a prime number, all coefficients – apart from 1 – are divisible by this prime number.'

We noticed with astonishment in the course of our search that we not only discovered the general connection between reciprocal numbers and natural logarithms but also the distinct feature that in this relation only the reciprocal prime numbers are important!

Pascal's Triangle, which explains mathematically the combinations involved in the board of nails, was in fact only rediscovered by Pascal. It had been known to the Moors for many centuries previously. Today, mathematicians generally consider it nothing but an interesting curiosity with no relevance to the present. The special knowledge of prime number coding should also have become common knowledge ever since it was formulated by E Kummer in the 19th Century.

Parts of the truth have therefore been known for some time and are generally accessible. Its real significance was not felt,

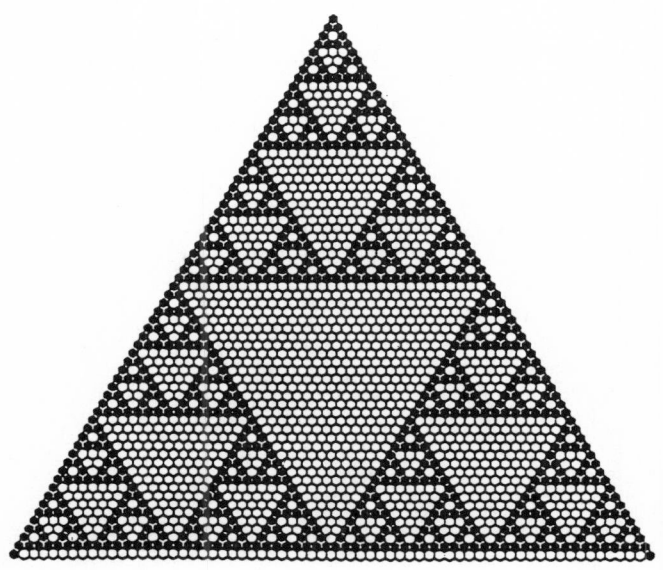

Figure 15

however, and it was therefore ignored.

Why is Pascal's Triangle coded in prime numbers?

Let us take a large 65-line Pascal's Triangle, called the Sierpinski Triangle. The Polish mathematician W Sierpinski was the first to stumble on the idea of indicating the divisibility of the individual Pascal numbers by the number 2 with the colours white and black (see figure 15 on previous page).

In this curious geometric object, the even numbers appear as white and the odd numbers as black (they are marked as hexagons). The geometry of this form is conspicuous because of the first 8 lines. They make up an equilateral triangle which repeats itself in a rhythm of eight lines.

The second conspicuous feature is the inverted white triangles which grow in size according to a special pattern.

The resulting geometry is referred to as fractal geometry. The term was first coined by B Mandelbrot (1975) as a name for the phenomenon of 'self-similarity'. A commonly quoted example is the surface of a cauliflower, where the shape of the whole is reflected in the shape of the smaller parts. Our first eight-line basic triangle is thus realized in larger triangles.

This first triangle which can be better described when enlarged (figure 16) contains a secret I had been looking for all my life.

The triangle consists of 36 = 6 x 6 hexagons. The first two lines are black, because they contain the odd number 1 three times (cf. figure 13).

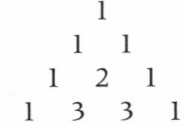

Figure 16

The third line shows a white hexagon in the centre because the number 2 is an even prime number. Because the fourth line again contains only odd numbers which gives an entirely black series, the resulting structure makes up the basis of the eight-line triangle. It is symmetrical and not only looks the same from all three sides, but recurs in the next biggest triangle exactly three times. This triangle is therefore again the same from all sides.

At the centre of these three similar triangles there is a fourth white triangle which is in axial symmetry to the three other triangles.

The first four lines of Pascal's Triangle create the following situation. The sum of the two ones gives the even prime number 2. Because of the two ones, only the numbers 1, 2 and 3 should appear in the following lines which determines that in the sixth line, in which the prime number 5 appears for the first time, the number 10 will appear twice. Because 10 is divisible by the prime number 5, the eighth line will be coded by the prime number 7 from this moment on because of the numbers 1, 2 and 3.

The first eight-line triangle doubles up to the sixteenth line, and at the same time the inverted white triangle increases in size. Fractal geometry must therefore remain coded in the prime numbers.

Just as the prime number twins 5 and 7, 11 and 13, etc. appear in the Prime Number Cross around a multiple of six, the reciprocal prime number twins in Pascal's Triangle are also linked to a geometry. This is expressed by the fact that all numbers of the line beginning with a prime number (not including the ones on the margin) which lie immediately before or after a number divisible by 6 are divisible by this prime number.

Because the number 1 has so far not been recognised as the base number of all prime numbers of the form $6n \pm 1$, and the numbers 2 and 3 are not of the form $6n \pm 1$, mathematicians were unable to see the connection between the prime numbers and the fractal geometry of Pascal's Triangle. They never recognized the elementary cycle of six in the prime numbers and were therefore also unable to find it in the reciprocal prime numbers.

189

It was not until 1994 that I myself realized that the inversion of a four-dimensional geometry which is derived from the base numbers 1, 2 and 3 and which has eight rays must again produce a geometry which is constructed on the numbers 1, 2 and 3, is triangular and has eight lines. The geometric form must, moreover, be triangular, which can only be illustrated by a hexagonal honeycomb form.

I had thus discovered the reciprocal geometry of the Prime Number Cross.

Scientists engaged in thermodynamics have attempted to describe collision processes among gas molecules using a form of mathematics which was completed over one hundred years ago. They did not suspect that a mole of a gas with its 10^{23} molecules represents a grid structure in which the colliding molecules are themselves the grid. Because the fundamental constant of the universe $e = 2.718$ is the order of the whole numbers in four-dimensional prime-number space, the reverse of e, the natural logarithm, must be somehow related to reciprocal numbers. And because the natural logarithm controls the decrease in prime numbers *ad infinitum* (prime number law), the prime numbers and the yes-no decisions in material processes are, on the other hand, connected via a fractal geometry which appears very strange to us.

Over the last few years, the mathematicians at the University of Bremen, including Professor H O Peitgen and his colleagues, have been vehemently asserting that the coding of Pascal's Triangle in prime numbers produces a geometry that cannot be a mathematical invention but is evidence of a profound system of the prime numbers in their relation to number theory.

Peitgen heads Chapter Six of his book (*Bausteine des Chaos*, Vol. 1) with a quotation from Spinoza: 'Nothing in nature is by chance ... Something appears to be chance only because of our lack of knowledge.'

Peitgen, however, does not bring this theme to its revolutionary conclusion because he also feels bound to observe the dogma that numbers are a 'human invention'. Geometry must therefore also be nothing more than human invention.

Despite Peitgen's great tact and diplomacy, the reaction of his fellow mathematicians is a mixture of wrath and indifference, for they fear that all dogma could be undermined by an acceptance of such theories.

But fractal geometry is not the only mathematical phenomenon that has a real existence in nature and is the reason the entropy of a gas is strictly linked to the natural logarithm. General geometry is also not a human invention. It is one realization of an expression of infinity in a finite way.

Certain conditions must be fulfilled for three-dimensional bodies to occur in four-dimensional space. For instance, only five different regular bodies may occur consisting either of three-, four- or five-angle forms (platonic bodies).

The fractal geometry of the Pascal geometry also provides an explanation for why a musical note, transferred from the string to the medium of air, should be transported through the chaos of colliding gas atoms (yes-no decisions) with such beautiful precision.

Pythagoras realized that the vibrations in the full, half, third, and quarter string of the monochord are in some way connected to the relationship existing between the whole numbers. Euler went one step further and integrated reciprocal prime numbers in his mathematical theory of music. The rules of halving, thirding and quartering of the string generally remained unknown, however. The whole elegance of the musical system has only now been revealed.

The gas medium with its reciprocal numerical order manages the transmission of music according to a fractal system containing eight stages. An octave is complete after eight steps. The whole secret of music theory is contained in the fact that the halving, three-part, five-part and seven-part of the string can be shown to result from there being two prime numbers which are not of the form $6n \pm 1$.

The human ear is specially constructed so that it can register fractal information transported through the air.

It should be emphasized once again that two physical spaces have to exist. The four-dimensional space around a point transports electromagnetic waves according to the order of the whole numbers. If a three-dimensional body is filled with air in such a four-dimensional space, this air will transport heat or sound according to the order of the reciprocal numbers. Both spaces are pure inversions, since for each whole number the infinite reciprocal value also exists. Both types of space are formed on the base numbers 1, 2 and 3 and on the structural number 8.

In chapter 6 of his book Professor Peitgen describes a game which I welcomed as a very precious gift.

If I allege that thermodynamics in its most fundamental form is based on the numbers 1, 2 and 3, I must accept that physicists will want to know about the experiments with which this can be conclusively proved. I was not aware of any such experiment until the summer of 1994.

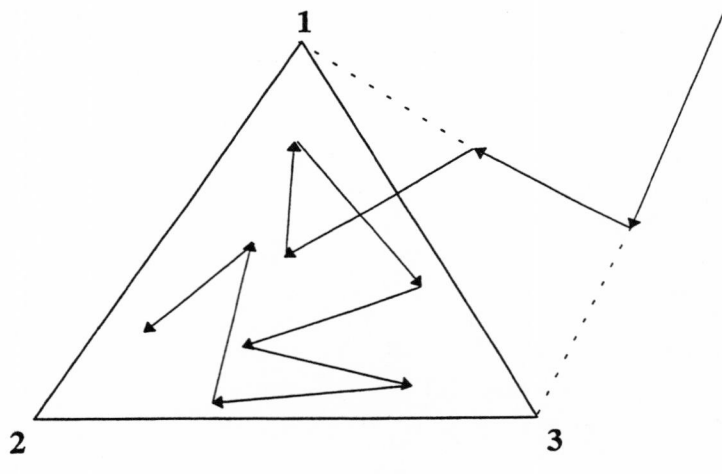

Figure 17

With the 'chaos game' I found the last missing link in the chain of proof.

We start out with a equilateral triangle whose corners are marked with the numbers 1, 2 and 3. Outside the triangle there is a tiny ball (eg a gas atom). A random generator which can only generate the numbers 1, 2 and 3 displays the first number and a connecting line is then drawn from the ball to the relevant corner of the triangle.

Half-way along the line we stop and again generate a random number. A connecting line is again drawn and again stopped half-way along the path. A short time later the ball will be inside the triangle and cannot leave it again as we continue the process. The ball now performs random zigzag movements in all directions.

So far we have only spoken of lines being drawn to help explain the game. In reality, however, it is not important that a (half) line is drawn. The only important thing is the sites at the ends of the half lines. These are marked by a point.

It is scarcely credible, but after approximately five hundred points have been marked a structure begins to emerge. After some thousand markings a form arises which could never have been anticipated. The recognition of this pattern was one of the most moving moments in my life. I had held green leaves in my hands thousands of times and had always been baffled by the question of who was controlling the order in this chaos. The pattern in this 'game of chance' came more and more to resemble a Sierpinski Triangle (figure 18).

Figure 18

Even Professor Peitgen could not contain his wonder when viewing the results of the chaos game:

> When [this figure] is seen for the first time, the viewer cannot believe his eyes. We have just witnessed the generation of the Sierpinski Triangle by a random generator. This is all the more astonishing as we had always considered the Sierpinski Triangle to be a classic example of structure and order. In other words, we have witnessed how random chance can generate an absolutely deterministic structure.

He attempted to find an explanation for the phenomenon of how fractal geometry can arise from the numbers 1, 2 and 3.

193

For his investigation he used the decimal system in the form of a pocket rule divided into decimetres, centimetres and millimetres and with which, for example, the three numbers 1, 2 and 3 were written together to make 123 (one hundred and twenty-three).

Without any knowledge of the special characteristics of the *e* numbers 2 and 3 he was nevertheless able to use the denominational number system to make a rather clumsy but correct explanation as to why black areas must appear in one position and fractal white patterns in another. What he could not have known was that he had discovered the true order of occupied three-dimensional space.

Why does the gas atom only travel half the distance in each of its random movements? The reason is that a gas atom in a container does not occur in isolation: it is constantly colliding with other gas atoms. Ideally it would collide with some other particle when half-way along its path from one location in the container to another, because the distance between two gas atoms is obviously always twice as long as half the distance. After the collision the two atoms would fly like billiard balls in new directions before colliding with two other atoms. The four atoms in the next collision would collide with four other atoms, then with 8, then 16, etc.

In reality, so many atoms collide with each other simultaneously in a gas-filled space that nobody would ever get the idea that the kinetics of colliding gas atoms in principle only involve dual collisions and thus yes-no decisions. The space they occupy thus behaves mathematically like the grid space that can be described by Pascal's Triangle.

The number theory regularities in Pascal's Triangle apply not only to the decimal system but to other counting systems (eg the system of 8 or 12). It has been observed in the Prime Number Cross, however, that when our familiar decimal system is taken as a base, the circles also increase according to this system. This is inherent in the structure of the six-rhythm of the prime numbers. As mentioned before, the number 6 is both the sum and the product of the base numbers 1, 2 and 3. The first six numbers are located in the prime number circle on the first quarter-circle (first quadrant). When this is completed to form a full circle (four quadrants), 1 x 2 x 3 must be multiplied with the following number 4 in the numeric order. This then gives us 24. This is the last number on the first circle.

If we add the following number 4 (1st + 2nd + 3rd + 4th quadrants) to the numbers 1 + 2 + 3, we obtain the number 10. With this number, 'one zero', the numerical sequence in our decimal system is finished. From now on, the 1 no longer has the value of a single unit, but now stands for ten (and later for one hundred, one thousand, etc.). And this number 'one zero' is the precise amount by which the sum of the numbers on the circles of the Prime Number Cross increase.

As long as mathematicians thought in lines and not in cycles, the number 10 could not be assigned any special significance.

I first received a decisive indication that Pascal's Triangle is also arranged according to the decimal system in February 1994 from a certain Rüdiger Gamm who is renowned in Germany as an arithmetical wizard. The young man had memorized all the powers of 2 to 14 for all the numbers up to 100 (eg 78 to the power of 13 = 78 × 78 × 78 × 78 × 78 × 78 × 78 × 78 × 78 × 78 × 78 × 78 × 78). He is, for instance, able to call up a 26-digit number from his head and then let it run in colour – just like on a television screen – in his head as a band of numbers. This 'band' can run at the speed of ten digits per second, either forwards or backwards.

Initially Rüdiger had learned these number bands off by heart, which in itself is incredible. I saw a demonstration of Rüdiger's art on television and immediately got in contact with him. I was extremely interested in testing whether his talent for visualization could be linked with mathematical mental operations.

A great counting genius of the last century, Zacharias Dase, mastered many sensational 'artistic feats'. He was, for example, able to calculate the number of a large amount of peas in a closed glass, simply by shaking the glass. He was also able to carry out complicated mathematical operations if they were based on the four basic modes of calculation. His major contributions to science were (at the instigation of Gauss) the very first calculation of the prime numbers between five and eight million (in his head!) and the computation of π to 200 places.

In 1994, I gave Rüdiger Gamm a 14-day course in the

rudiments of chemistry and mathematics.

I then showed him a new method of calculating the periodic reciprocal values for the numbers of the form 6 ± 1 (including to any number of places after the decimal point).[1] With a simple calculating trick, the last digit of the period can be determined and then all remaining numbers computed by continuous multiplication from right to left (Hans Jäckel). Until then, these numbers had to be calculated by single-division operations. It is thus possible to recognize merely from the periodic length of the decimal fraction of the odd numbers whether the relevant whole number is a prime number.

This is normally totally impossible without using pen and paper for anything more than a hundred-digit decimal. Because Rüdiger has a photographic memory, he managed these operations in a very brief time. He then stored the individual steps in an 'auxiliary memory' until he could transfer the final result to his 'main memory'. It is fascinating to witness how he can read off from his head numbers of a periodic fraction with hundreds of digits with closed eyes.

During his coaching, I introduced him to Pascal's Triangle. He immediately read the numbers not as individual digits, but registered them at a glance as powers of the number 11.

$$
\begin{array}{ccccccccc}
 & & & & 1 & & & & \rightarrow & 1 = 11^0 \\
 & & & 1 & & 1 & & & \rightarrow & 11 = 11^1 \\
 & & 1 & & 2 & & 1 & & \rightarrow & 121 = 11^2 \\
 & 1 & & 3 & & 3 & & 1 & \rightarrow & 1331 = 11^3 \\
1 & & 4 & & 6 & & 4 & & 1 \rightarrow & 14631 = 11^4 \\
 & & & & \vdots & & & &
\end{array}
$$

Figure 19

When he reached the sixth row he suddenly hesitated. He was not able to read this line as a single number because of the 2-digit numbers it contained.

$$1 \quad 5 \quad 10 \quad 10 \quad 5 \quad 1$$

I showed him that the power series of the number 11 is not interrupted. Because the numbers 10 occur in the sixth line for the first time we must therefore again make use of the method of transformation. When the numbers of the sixth row are imagined in a decimal positional system, we must work from right to left and replace all numbers over 9, just as 10-pence coins are changed into a one pound coin. The result for our sixth row is the decimal number: 1 6 1 0 5 1 = 11^5.

This procedure can be repeated any number of times.

Rüdiger Gamm had unconsciously given me the decisive thrust for my line of argument.

Pascal's Triangle is therefore coded in a positional system. It contains the sequence of ordered numbers, read from the top both to the bottom left and to the bottom right.

$$1, 2, 3, 4, 5, 6, 7, 8, 9, 10, 11, 12 \ldots$$

If the numbers are read as one number from left to right, the numerical sequence (1, 2, 3, ...) on the left side acquires another value within the framework of the whole numbers from row to row.

1	1
2	10
3	100
4	1000
5	10000
	⋮

This decimal increase corresponds in the Prime Number Cross to the reduction of the decimal fraction (written without a point)

$$\frac{1}{81} = 0\ 0\ 1\ 2\ 3\ 4\ 5\ 6\ 7\ 8\ 9\ (10)\ (11)\ (12) \ldots$$

In the case of the numerical sequence of ordered numbers being read towards the bottom right, the positional value does not change. All ordered numbers (1, 2, 3, ...) are on the ten-position (in the positional system).

$$10, 20, 30, 40, 50 \ldots$$

The correlation between all essential coordinating elements in the Prime Number Cross and those of the reciprocal Pascal's Triangle is therefore complete.

NOTE

1 From ancient times until modern, there has been only one method of calculating prime numbers (the 'sieve of Eratosthenes'). We were able to show that there had to be a second method of determining the prime numbers.

For mathematicians: the test whether a number is not a prime number is made with the aid of Fermat's Minor Theorem. Because we have been able to decipher the undiscovered foundation of this law – which was proved by Euler – from the prime number coding of Pascal's Triangle, it is a proven fact that the periodic length of all reciprocal numbers are coded. Conversely, it can also be shown why the existence of Wilson's Law can only be explained by means of the Prime Number Cross.

CHAPTER SEVENTEEN

GOD IS BACK!

The consequences arising from a recognition of the fact that there are two forms of space are far-reaching. Not only will the theory of the Big Bang now have to be totally discarded, which in itself will mean that a vast number of textbooks and schoolbooks have to be rewritten, the 'modern' theory of evolution which can be described as a very contrived result of the Big Bang will be put under an irrievable death sentence by the new findings from chemistry and mathematics. It has become the 'pet' of many scientists who would be happy and grateful to be able to use such theories to expel God from the world and from their lives.

In the 19th century, the theory of evolution replaced the notion that a personal God created the plants, animals and finally humankind at the end of his creation. The new theory was rational from a scientific point of view. Because mutations in plants and animals can be observed repeatedly, and the violence of nature (eg climatic change) offered a possible explanation for natural selection, the creation of life – from primitive single-cell organisms all the way to human beings – was commonly believed to be a series of coincidences. This belief has not been refuted until now.

An American chemist once wrote about an alien returning from a visit to our planet who was asked about the creatures he had seen, and replied: 'There are indeed innumerable insects on the continents which have increased to unimaginably large populations. Apart from these creatures who control the planet, there is also a small number of "other" lifeforms which are of totally different form and are sometimes quite large. These are the other animals and the humans.'

The theory of evolution also consigned the origins of insects – the largest group of creatures on this planet – to chance. The historical development of insects, ever since they acquired the ability to fly, took three geological ages: the upper Carboniferous, the Permian and the upper Cretaceous. In the third age, which was approximately 65 million years ago, the final development occurred parallel with the development of flowering plants.

The course of an insect's existence also runs through three stages – **egg**, **larva**, **insect.**

Only because of the enormous number and triple aspect of the insects is the smaller section of inhabitants from the second group able to exist at all.

The body of an insect consists of **head, thorax**, and **abdomen.** The thorax contains the two-times-three legs (and the wings). Insects, of which there are 800,000 (!) different species (not to speak of the different types of each species), are flying creatures and have a head made of six segments and faceted eyes which, although they cannot focus, can process information ten times more quickly. This is essential to their navigation in flying. The facets are hexagonal!

The insect's 'armour' consists of a material containing sugar. The sugars consist of the sixth element, carbon, and they have a special molecular structure. This has a cyclic hexagonal form.

The second, smaller group of animals has a skeleton and eyes which with the help of a lens are able to focus objects on a retina. The bodies of these vertebrates (and of humans) also consist of three parts: the **head**, the **torso**, and the **extremities.**

The third part, the extremities, which are here classified as a part of the body, are of three types: 4 legs; 2 legs and 2 arms; or 2 legs and 2 arms refunctioned as wings. Their development after fertilization does not follow a three-stage cycle of physical development but the three possibilities of protecting the maternal organism from the foreign protein of the foetus: **egg, sac, womb**.

Is it of particular significance that there are two major groups of beings? Because I had been studying the question of double space for many years, I immediately suspected that life on this planet could be mathematically subject to the conditions of these two forms of space.

The conspicuous feature of insects is the number of times 6 appears in any description of them. The three-part torso of a bee and its six legs consist of chitin, an ingenious 'synthetic' substance that is digestible because it is made of hexagonal sugar structures. This animal collects nectar (sugar, which, of course, is not related to our industrial sugar) and stores it in hexagonal hives.

If a flying insect is compared with a flying animal from the second group – eg a swallow – it can be shown that both are built to suit the space in which they happen to live.

The structure and the function of the insect incorporates three-dimensional gas-filled space, which is determined by the base numbers 1, 2, 3 and the number 6^1.

A swallow is constructed entirely differently. It has no armour of hexagonal sugar – instead it has a skeleton made of inorganic carbon salts. It can see its prey and follow it. It lives in a space in which it can recognize three-dimensional objects for what they are (eg a church tower and the landscape).

Humans also see objects in perspective. Man can look into the sky towards the infinity that surrounds him but he cannot perceive the infinity of the sky. The sky appears to him a three-dimensional space like a dome.

He is made for four-dimensional space, even if he has not become conscious of this space until now.

The insect lives in a three-dimensional world and is also not aware of it. Because gas-filled three-dimensional space is its habitat and it is constructed according to these mathematical laws, the objects it sees in this space can only be two-dimensional. Regardless of whether insects are swarming in front of a blade of grass, an apple or a church tower, for them there are only two-dimensional areas. The fly therefore does not care whether it is sitting on the ground, creeping up or down the wall or even crawling on the ceiling. It has no consciousness of the third dimension.

Because there are two forms of space, there must also be a life form for each space prescribed by mathematics. This new zoological perspective will at last also promote understanding of the highly developed social structures existing among ants or bees. All theoretical evolutionists who have given serious attention to insect communities admit at least indirectly that their notion of coincidence fails when they wish to interpret the development of such ordered states.

The proverbial 'ant colony', which seems to be so much superior to our political structures yet is nevertheless a nightmare, turns out to be the highest life form in a world that is foreign to us. The solution to this problem is in the prime numbers.

Just as an insect has no comprehension of the third dimension, we humans are also unable to comprehend the fourth dimension. However, because we are conscious of ourselves, we are able to draw logical conclusions from recognized mathematical laws: if there has to be a fourth dimension, this higher and final dimension must have a form of consciousness beyond the bounds of our consciousness. Since the dawn of time, this notion has gone under the name of 'God'.

The ten years I had allotted myself for finding my direction on the way to solve the 'riddle of the universe' had long passed. Despite the pains I had undergone and the great exhaustion, I was euphoric.

Christina had in the meantime obtained a position as a doctor in the south of Germany, and Michael had also retired for a while in order to write his thesis. The proof he used in this work was so unusual that it was submitted for an expert opinion to one of the leading professors in applied mathematics in Germany, Professor Butzer at the Technical College of Aachen. This man immediately declared the proof to be correct and made sure that Michael became the first PhD candidate at the Mathematical Institute of the University of Dortmund to be awarded the grade 'excellent'.

I was now busy organizing the printing of the first volume of *The Prime Number Cross*.

It proved almost impossible to stop me from my concentrated research in mathematical problems. The old trick in such situations of switching the field of study worked in this case too.

I still remember the words my father said to me when I was 15: '... then find this fuel and patent it together with the disk.' When I synthesized the silane oils at the age of 30 I was not aware that I had already found 'this fuel'. As a visionary of space travel I had been searching for it for so long. In retrospect it seems unbelievable that at the time I only registered and received a patent for the higher silicone hydrides. But this 'internal block' turned out to be a blessing, as later the oil was still unknown as a fuel.

In order to obtain a patent for a single-stage reusable rocket, a proposal had to be put to the German patent office that was convincing in all technical points. But some technical details were still missing from the 'multipatent' that I was now looking for. I slowly began to see how ridiculous it was that I had been postponing a boyhood dream for the past 35 years and constantly finding new excuses for not realizing it.

The deadlock was resolved when an engineer appeared in my life – again the right person at the right time. Walter Büttner was a former pilot of jet aircraft and had enough knowledge of the subject to be able to help me solve the outstanding problem.

In Ingrid Bergmannshoff I found a new partner for the next stage of my life. Despite great demands from her work in her pharmacy, she devoted many hours of her precious time to support me at the computer. Finally, in 1992, I was able to dictate to her the patent registration and submit it to the German patent office without requiring the assistance of a patent lawyer.

Conventional, superimposed rocket cylinders have to carry their whole starting weight on a rocket jet, and therefore very quickly use up their fuel. This in turn makes them lighter and faster until they are finally burned out. From the physical and mathematical point of view, this process takes place according to an equation in which the constant e again occurs and which is called the rocket equation.

I had one advantage over rocket physicists in that I had discovered the direct connection between the number π and the Euler number e. Whereas they continued to construct rockets along the linear principle and their technology had long been stagnating, the disk-shaped rocket working according to a cyclic principle offered the possibility of using the surrounding air to elegantly carry the weight of the whole rocket.

203

In order to put a disk into the air – with a full tank of rocket fuel – no energy-wasting rocket thrust, but only a turbine ring – ie rotating blades – was needed. The turbine head would be driven by four jet turbines arranged in cruciform fashion to each other. These would be placed inside the disk, draw in air from the top, and run on normal petrol. To prevent the disk from turning with the screw, two counter-rotating turbine rings would be added.

Even the optical similarity between the Prime Number Cross on the one hand, and the form and function of the disk on the other is astonishing and certainly no coincidence. The fact that discussion on flying saucers has refused to go away since the end of the Second World War is also definitely no coincidence.

Because the disk can hover and glide it cannot fall out of the sky either when flying or when landing.

The problem in space travel is not only to lift off in the first place but to reach a speed of approximately 30,000 km per hour. A conventional rocket reaches this speed after its vertical take-off. When the three stages have burnt out, they fall back towards Earth and are burned up in our atmosphere. Hundreds of millions of dollars have been burned up in this way. The Space Shuttle programme was intended to put an end to this cost madness, but the opposite actually happened.

The rocket disk is not thrust upwards, but flung laterally, as is familiar from the sport of discus-throwing. After the disk has reached the speed of 300 km per hour, the air will carry the weight of the whole fully-tanked vessel. To prevent the turbine ring from disturbing the aerodynamics of the disk, it is surrounded by a hydraulic movable exterior layer, whose elements will be reeled in after this speed has been reached. There will then be no need for lift provided by the turbine ring.

If conventional, very light and voluminous heavy gas with unimaginably dangerous combination characteristics were to be used as fuel, the vessel would simply be too big. A rocket disk would require as fuel an oil with a high specific weight and high energy, so that it could be kept as small as possible.

By taking the 'long way' and with ever-increasing speed in an ever-decreasing atmospheric resistance, this craft would evade the rocket equation. My merger of mathematics and physics was totally new with regard to rocket physics and the patent office did not raise any objections. Trying to sell a patent to the aerospace industry would, of course, be a different matter.

The far-sighted members of the boards of German industries were never able to accept something really new. One by one they consigned the patent to their development departments where it was predictably confronted with iron resistance.

After the mandatory period of 18 months had elapsed, it was clear that a patent would be granted. A possible breakthrough in space travel was now plausible when linked to this new knowledge of the very fundamentals of physics. I had formerly not worried very much about why I had always been equally passionate about different subjects which, according to common understanding, had very little to do with each other. But now I knew the reason. All of these actually did have something to do with each other. It was a great joy for me to watch all the different pieces of the puzzle of my life merge to form a wonderful mosaic.

It seemed as if the matter was now being moved by an unseen hand, for soon two men who had both read *The Prime Number Cross* got in touch with me.

The engineer, Dr Klaus Kunkel, spontaneously offered to bear the costs of obtaining a worldwide patent; this was the first step towards preventing the American armaments industry from transforming this 'flying saucer' into a flying bomb at no costs to themselves. We all well remembered how the liquid rocket A4 (called V2) invented by the German engineer Dr Wernher von Braun in Germany was exploited for military purposes by Americans and Russians.

Professor Dieter Straub, holder of the chair in thermodynamics at an institute for rocket physics, undertook the presentation of the idea to some management groups in the German aeronautics and space industry.

And then something unexpected happened. Because the criticism made by some gentlemen was so fierce and emotional or their indifference was so obviously contrived, a certain righteous wrath arose in me, my own explosive fuel that would drive me to find the answer to another secret of this planet.

The Earth is covered by a shell of air which is roughly 20 per cent oxygen and 80 per cent nitrogen. This ratio of constituents is not only fortunate for us, it is also absolutely necessary for life.

The oxygen and nitrogen molecules both contain a deep secret. The magnetic power of oxygen had always been of interest to me. I had so far had no special 'relationship' with the nitrogen molecule. It has a triple bond and, according to the rules of chemistry, it should be so unstable that our planet should normally consist of silicon nitride and not silicate bonds, the compounds of oxygen.

It had been clear to me since I was 30 that the essence of silane oil must have something to do with the phenomenon of lightning in atmospheric storms.

When diluted bromine solution was dropped into highly diluted trisilane at a temperature of −100°C (1968 in Cologne), electrical circular flashes had been discharged over the drop points. At that time we were working with a pure nitrogen atmosphere. When I used the much more aggressive chlorine instead of bromine and the explosion occurred in the laboratory, I was again able to observe – through my bullet-proof helmet and the thin protective glass – an electric flash before the blast of the explosion hit me.

The detonation at that time had a long-lasting effect on me which I never discussed with anybody afterwards. I did not know which element had reacted so drastically with the highly diluted silane. The few drops of chlorine solution at −100°C had acted as priming, but after the explosion this solution had all been blown away. Again this time only pure oxygen had surrounded the solution.

How does lightning happen? Without the millions of lightning discharges each day there would be no life on this planet. Plants require fertilization with nitrates if they are to produce their 20 amino acids. If nitrates do not naturally occur in the earth, the nitrogen in the atmosphere must constantly open its tripartite compounds through frictional electrons and react with oxygen to form nitrogen oxide. The rain washes out the resulting nitric acid and carries the nitrogen compound to the earth. It all works so well because the triple bond in the nitrogen molecule remains stable in the presence of all other chemical influences. Scientists have always only been able to register and describe this process.

In my oral exam for physics I had been asked by Professor Hauser whether I had any explanation as to why silicon could not form any double bonds as carbon did. Three elements can form single, double and triple bonds: carbon, oxygen and nitrogen. Silicon has not got this power because only three elements were provided with the power of forming three different types of bonds. Chemistry is – like the other two natural sciences – the material costume for mathematics with which infinity is made finite.

I now began to see the circle close. Because silicon cannot form multiple bonds, nitrogen can only react in one way with this chemical.

Back in the 1920s, a chemist demonstrated for the first time that nitrogen at a temperature of over 1,400°C reacts with silicon to form powdery, very stable silicon nitride. Energy is released in this process.

Carbon reacts with nitrogen at very high temperatures to form a triple bond. Energy is consumed in this process.

Silicon therefore burns with nitrogen whereas carbon does not. It would, however, be pointless to use powdery silicon as rocket fuel. What is required is a pumpable chemical compound of silicon, and a new rocket design. If silane oil is brought to a reaction with compressed air in a furnace, the oxygen in the air will burn the hydrogen of the silane oils at a temperature of 3,000°C. Because the nitrogen releases its triple bonds at this temperature and under this pressure, the nitrogen radicals attack the gaseous silicon and burn it.

Silicon nitride has a molecular weight eight times that of water. The combustion of silane oils in air therefore provides an effective rocket thrust. The special thing about this process is that an oxidation agent need no longer be carried.

Aircraft flying with jet engines have to bear the burden of the nitrogen used as reaction agent in the combustion chambers, which leads to a high loss of energy. However, the nitrogen also cools the turbine blades which would otherwise overheat. It would be more practical to use rocket motors for air traffic. It would then be possible to work with a much higher temperature in the combustion chamber. However, a rocket aircraft would have to carry its oxidation agent with a resulting loss in capacity for useful load (eg passengers).

Carbon's reaction with oxygen therefore maintains metabolism in animal life on this planet. The carbon-oxygen

207

compounds are disjointed by plants. Silicon, the 'brother' of carbon, was only discovered during the 20th century and initially became known as a material for rectifiers, transistors and diodes, and later for computer chips. The 'brother' (in the atmosphere) of oxygen, nitrogen, now serves – in reaction with silicon – as a future fuel for air and space transport.

In the autumn of 1994, I and Dr Kunkel registered a radically novel type of rocket engine and a rocket long-distance aircraft (5,000–8,000 kilometres per hour at a height of over 50 kilometres) at the patent office.

In order to travel the distance from New York to Tokyo, a passenger must reckon on a whole day's travelling. Although we live in a world and at a time that has seen continuous increases in speed, it has so far been impossible for aircraft to cross half the world in a few hours.

It was clear to me that the secret of the triple bond of nitrogen should be made accessible to the public only when people are prepared to recognize that a divine plan for our universe exists. Perhaps we can only have optimum space travel when we have comprehended the law of the universe.

There can therefore be no coincidence in nature. Everything has a meaning, even if we cannot always recognize it at first. I finally grasped this fact in 1994, and this certainty and belief in the correctness and elegance of the divine order gave me the confidence I needed to pursue from now on only that to which I had always felt myself drawn.

I often allowed my former life to pass before me as if in a film. It was incredible how much the individual pieces of knowledge had come together to form a harmonious whole. The loneliness of the last 15 years had had a reason. But was it still necessary?

I had always hoped to meet a woman who was capable of accepting the variety of my interests and the complexity of my personality, as well as able to inspire me and bring more fun and joy into my life. This potentially insoluble task was solved at the drop of a hat by my guardian angel. I met Walburga Posch, later to be my co-author. She had also been overwhelmed with profound why-questions ever since her childhood. In contrast to me, however, she had found her answers in spiritual areas.

We went on holidays together. For the first time in my life I no longer felt the need for constant and deep thought and calculation. Instead, I simply felt good and knew that it was also the right time for it.

It seemed that the time had at last arrived when the idea that had first been formulated during my visit to Professor Ley could finally be realized – the book aimed at the general public.

I had received an offer from a publisher of technical books to write an account of the deciphering of prime numbers and the consequences. The intended size of the publication and the advertising budget meant that the book would turn out to be just one among thousands of other publications. The general readership would not be reached – and I therefore rejected the offer.

A short time later, in October 1994, the film producer Frieder Mayrhofer introduced me to the daughter of the owner of one of Germany's largest publisher groups. By 'coincidence', he was also the owner of the publishing house of technical books whose offer I had rejected. This woman recognized the importance of the subject, read my books in a few days, and informed her father. He immediately invited me to a meeting.

When I describe my ideas there is always the danger that a listener might find the complex mixture of science and mathematics exhausting after a short time. I therefore chose an approach that would not so much impress the publisher with details as surprise him.

An important author of technical books, Professor Hoimar von Ditfurth, had died a few years previously, and in an interview recorded shortly before his death he had spoken of his passionate wish to cast a glance behind the 'great curtain'. He had looked through large telescopes into the depths of the universe and had visited the giant laboratories of particle physics underneath the surface of the Earth. He had, however, been unable to discover what really lay behind this physical world. He would have given an arm or leg, or several years of his life, for such knowledge.

I told this story, which had fascinated me, to the publisher.

He was fascinated

'Mr Plichta, are you telling me that von Ditfurth was convinced that there is a secret puzzle hidden behind this world?'

209

I answered, 'Yes. It was one of his great achievements to admit it!'

'And have you solved anything of this puzzle?'

'Yes!'

'And what have you discovered?'

'The significance of the prime numbers in the resolution of cosmic theory.'

I then spoke briefly about the role of prime numbers in coding systems used by banks, insurance companies, secret services, and atomic missiles.

'Because modern sophisticated computers can decipher any code, secret data is coded with 50-digit prime numbers. This is the only means of secure coding, for even the most modern computers would take years to crack this code.

'It is amazing', I continued, 'that we in the computer age code our secrets in prime numbers without suspecting that nature, even the entire universe is coded in prime numbers!'

'Could you tell me in one sentence what is the real significance of your scientific work?'

We looked at each other and both of us noticed how tense the atmosphere in the room had suddenly become.

I formulated my words clearly and slowly: 'It was a decisive mistake that science began to interpret numbers as a human invention approximately 100 years ago, just so that mysticism could be expelled from science and mathematics. In this way God was also expelled from nature.'

'Do you mean to tell me that God is back?'

'I think that would be one way to express it. It is, of course, impossible to prove God's existence. I can, however, prove that there is a divine structural plan behind this world. In this way the Big Bang and the apparently coincidental creation of life will be consigned to a period of our history from which we have now emerged. No great stretch of the imagination is needed to guess the effect this will have on the book market.'

There was silence for a moment.

'Could you write a bestseller for me within three months?'

'Yes, I certainly could!'

'We will then use all means in our power to make sure this book reaches its readers. Go and write the book!'

NOTE

1 An equally remarkable phenomenon, which is also one of nature's great secrets, is the variety of forms displayed by the snowflake. The formation of these crystals can only occur in air at a certain minus temperature. Photographic recordings give ample evidence of the beauty of these crystals, and of their hexagonal structure. Again nobody seems to care why the element of 6 should also occur here.

EPILOGUE

The English philosopher John Wycliffe, who lived in the 14th century, held the opinion that God is not provided with absolute freedom and power, but that even He is restricted by divine order and laws. Three centuries before Spinoza and Leibniz the old platonic notion was already being resurrected – that the world can be no different from the way it actually is.

In this book we have avoided coming to dialectic grips with the idea of the random creation of natural law by a big bang, simply because the elegance of a plan for the universe based on prime number will automatically assign the Big Bang theory to the realms of history. I would only like to discuss the question of how it came to pass that such a theory could even be formulated and become so universally accepted. So accepted, indeed, that in the end the general public was left in absolutely no doubt that this was no theory but rather a scientifically proven truth.

The construction of giant reflecting telescopes and radio telescopes has allowed our knowledge of the universe to grow to hitherto undreamed of dimensions. And at the same time as this discovery first got going, a new branch of physics was born – particle physics. This had its origins in nuclear physics and took as its subject extremely short-lived phenomena. These could only be seen as vapour trails on photographs but were nonetheless designated as (material) particles.

Two different strands of physics thus came into fashion, one dealing with the immeasurably remote and large and the other dealing with the infinitesimally short-lived and small. These have some things in common, however. Both are capable of swallowing entire national budgets and each one is in itself contradictory. For one thing, we have the increasing red-shift of objects speeding away from us, whose interpretation is actually quite questionable, and on the other hand we have the particle zoo, the photographs of which mockingly remind us of the shadows in Plato's cave allegory. The comparison becomes all the more inescapable when the particles are named with letters of the Greek alphabet.

Then came that ingenious marketing trick – the story of the first three minutes – which connected the practical scientific and business instincts of both of these extremely different directions in physics.

Out of compressed energy a spherical structure was suddenly formed. Time and space were born. Between the zero point in time and a fraction of the first second, all the minute particles and antiparticles that we know from our laboratory experiments were created. As an inversion of this unimaginably short time, began unimaginably long time that allows the astrophysicists of today to receive light signals billions of years old.

Computer animation in which the beginning is drawn out and the rest contracted in time gives these assumed events a realistic appearance, especially for the gullible young.

Criticism of this theory, which has generally come from disciplines outside physics, was discounted as unqualified from the very start. Only that which can be measured can be accepted as true. And it is precisely this belief that has caused us – in the course of the greatest struggle the world has ever seen, that between belief and knowledge – to stumble once more into a trap. We have stopped believing in a divine order and have started believing instead in the indisputable value of our measurements and our interpretation. One of the greatest thinkers of the West warned us against this fallacy: 'We see the sun wandering across the sky, but this interpretation by human intellect is nevertheless incorrect. If we can arm our eyes with microscopes or telescopes, we shall still not be able to run away from this misinterpretation caused by our intellect.'

Since our intellect is locked into a finite mode of perception this book has sought a way to replace the finite nature of our thought with a logical-mathematical infinite perspective, which is inseparably tied to John Wycliffe's divine law.

INDEX

acoustics 178
alternating series 184–5
amino acids 40, 41–3, 92, 93, 94, 96, 100, 124, 131–2, 144, 148, 206
Archimedes 136, 167
Asimov, I 34
astronomy 71, 103
atomic bomb 14, 28, 125, 135, 145
atomic model, Bohr's 155, 157
atomic nucleus 29, 31, 80, 86, 134, 136, 146, 157–8, 160
atomic numbers 31, 33, 42, 67, 132, 133, 136
atomic weight 31
atoms 14, 18, 67, 105, 106, 109, 122, 151, 174
atoms, asymmetric 19, 62, 63, 64, 67, 79, 81, 101
atoms, Newton's theory of 105–6

Babylonians 126–7
bases 144
beryllium 31, 33, 42, 133
Big Bang theory 2, 5, 25, 38, 127, 199, 210
binomial coefficients 182, 186, 187
binomials 172, 186, 187
biochemistry 40, 43, 92
biology 10, 41, 51
bismuth 30, 31, 33, 122
Böhme, H 90, 98–101, 142, 47
Bohr, N 158, 160–1
Braun, W von 50, 51, 205
Bruno, G 11, 105

calculus, differential and integral 144, 175, 176

carbon 33, 38, 39, 201, 207
carbon monoxide 98
cgs system 26, 155
Champollion, J F 13, 14
chance chains 181
chaos game 173, 192
chaos theory 180
chemistry 2, 3, 10, 15, 16, 17, 50, 166, 207
chemistry, stereo- 92, 93, 94, 100, 108
chitin 201
chlorophyll 23, 144
chromium 33, 58
circle with radius 137
coincidence 92, 202, 208, 209
collision process, kinetic 179
combination analysis 174
consonants 41, 47n, 84, 116
construction plan 43, 92, 95, 174
coordination compounds 96
Creation 92, 116
Curie, M and P 32, 35
Cusanus, N 105

Darwin, G H 55
Dase, Z 195
decimal fractions, periodic 167
decimal fractions, recurring 167
decimal system/base-10 system 26, 116, 123, 124, 126, 143–4, 145, 153, 155, 165, 194, 195
Dedekind, J W 5
dimensions 110–11, 130, 160, 169
Ditfurth, H von 209
DNA 68, 110, 144
dogma/dogmatism 3, 105, 126–7
double bonds 207
divine trinity, see trinity

Earth–Moon system 55, 60n,
103, 139
eclipses 141
electron pair bonding 22
electron shells 68, 104, 117, 134,
136, 155
electron theory 76, 86
electron twins 22, 69, 115, 120,
151
electrons 22, 29, 39, 35, 54, 68,
71, 104, 109, 113–15, 122,
130, 135, 158, 160, 161
electrons, four types of 68, 69,
109
electromagnetic energy 27, 28,
45, 129, 131, 154
elements, chemically stable 34,
122, 123–4, 136
elements, exclusively artificial 34
elements, naturally radioactive
34
elements, unstable 136
energy 27, 130, 213
energy, square of 129
Einstein, A 11, 25, 27, 28, 43,
44, 69, 77, 86, 126, 156, 163
Einstein's formula 126, 128, 129,
143
entropy 48n, 191
ephedrine 99–100
Eratosthenes, sieve of 197n
Euler, L 5, 112, 162, 172, 191,
198
Euler–Mascheroni constant 177
Euler's number 6, 7, 26, 137,
167, 178, 203
evolution, theory of 86, 199

Fehér, F 58, 59, 61, 65, 70, 77,
78, 79, 81, 82
Felten, M 170–5, 202
Fermat's Minor Theorem 198n
Fischer, E O 19, 56, 58, 142–5,
147
four dimensions 109
fuel (rocket fuel) 20, 21, 49–53,
204

Galton Board/board of nails 180,
183–4, 187
Gamm, R 195–7
gas medium 178, 184, 185, 191
Gauss C F 5, 6, 11, 112, 167,
168, 170, 195
Gauss distribution curve 181,
183
Gay Lussac, J L 44
geometry, fractal 187, 189, 190,
191, 193
geometry, reciprocal 178, 186
geometry atoms, asymmetric 19,
65
God 6, 10, 42, 49, 69, 86, 104,
105, 107, 144, 163, 175, 199,
202, 210
gravity, theory of 103

Hadamard, J 6, 166, 169, 171n
haeme 96, 97, 98, 101, 142
haemoglobin 96, 98, 101, 144
Hahn, O 14, 75, 82
Hahn-Einstein equation 72
Hauser, U 75, 86, 110
Heisenberg, W 69
Hermite, C 5, 166
Herr, W 67, 70, 75, 82
hieroglyphs 116
hydrogen 20, 30, 33, 38, 54, 64,
65, 132, 145
hydrogen bomb 14, 126
hysterisis loops 96

infinitely large/small 162–3, 212
infinity 5, 29, 106, 115, 131,
154, 191, 201
infinity, triple 153, 158
insects 199–201
iron atom 33
isotope frequency 31, 32, 133
isotope number 132
isotopes, double 133–4
isotopes, pure 42, 133–4

Jäckel, H 196
jet propulsion 207

215

John of the Cross, St 120, 163

Kant, I 29, 36*n*, 104, 107, 170
Karlson, P 94, 95, 101*n*
Kepler, J 103, 143, 144
Kunkel, K 205, 208

language groups 84
Lavoisier, A de 14
Lay, R 1, 2, 3, 4, 5, 9, 11, 126, 209
Leibniz, G W 3, 5, 11, 70, 105, 106, 112, 119, 175, 185*n*, 212
Leonardo da Vinci 51, 53, 54
ligands 96, 97
light energy 179
light, speed of 25, 26, 27, 28, 74, 131, 149, 151, 153, 154, 163
l-isoleucine and l-threonine 93, 94
logarithm, integral 169
logarithm, natural 6, 144, 168, 169, 176, 177–8, 184, 185*n*, 187, 190, 191
logic 2, 8, 174

magnesium atom 33, 144, 145
Mandelbrot, B 188
material world 3
mathematicians 162, 166, 190
mathematics 4, 5, 8, 11, 41, 43, 71, 80, 107, 112, 125, 149, 160, 166–8, 207
mathematics, three–dimensional 80
Mercator series 184
metal atom, zerovalent 57, 97, 142
mirror forms 108
monads 105, 106
month, sidereal and sidonic 55, 56, 60*n*, 138
monochord 191
Moon 50, 55, 60*n*, 68, 82, 83, 141, 144, 154, 155
moon dust 82, 83, 141
Mössbauer, R 146, 147–8

natural constants 26, 27, 122, 127, 136*n*, 137, 158
neutrons 29, 31, 68, 135–6, 158
Newton, I 5, 29, 103, 104, 106, 107, 140, 172, 175
nitrogen 33, 39, 205, 206, 207
Nobel Prize 19, 49, 50, 58, 59, 69, 75, 135, 142, 144, 145, 146
nuclear chemistry 30, 43, 67
nuclear resonance spectrum 19
number circles 120
number, concept of 29, 95, 166
number, even and uneven 150
number *i*, imaginary 168, 174
number theory 69, 92, 109, 112, 113, 135
number twins 113
numbers, rational, irrational and transcendental 26
numeric sequence, reciprocal 106
numeric space, four-dimensional 121
numeric space, shell-shaped 121

oestral cycle 55
order in disorder 185
oxygen 31, 33, 38, 39, 54, 60*n*, 96, 98, 205, 206

particle zoo 106, 212
Pascal, B 182, 187
Pascal numbers 186
Pascal's Triangle 182, 184, 186, 187, 188, 189, 190, 194, 195, 196, 197, 198
Petigen, H O 190, 193
peptides, peptide chains 92, 93, 96, 97
Periodic Table 18, 33, 34, 36*n*, 53, 132, 134, 136, 142, 145, 164
pharmacology 88, 90, 91, 99, 101
pharmacy 73, 74
philosophy 71, 125

photon 154
physics 2, 10, 50, 69, 71, 74,
    127, 158, 160, 166
physics, atomic 74
physics, astro- and particle
    physics 212
Planck, M 43, 69, 74, 77, 158
Planch-Einstein formula 72, 74n,
    87, 157
planets 103, 105, 106
Plato 11, 108, 212
platonic body 191
platonic tradition 69, 212
Plichta, H (*née* Ring) 37, 63, 72,
    73, 88–90, 91, 102, 103
porphyrin rings 142
Posch, W 208–10
primates 86, 91, 92
Prime Number law 6, 166, 168,
    190
prime number sequence 113,
    114, 117, 178
prime number space 129
prime number twins 113, 115,
    116, 146, 189
prime numbers, distribution of
    169
prime numbers, even 114, 187,
    189
prime numbers, structure of 122,
    154
primordial soup 91–2, 93, 96
protons 29, 30, 31, 35, 54, 67,
    68, 79, 130, 135, 158
promethium 30, 33
pyrolysis 78
Pythagoras 11, 150, 191
Pythagorean numbers 127, 143

quadrants 108, 176, 194
quadrupole magnet 97, 142
quantum mechanics 71, 74n, 76,
    91, 92, 146, 147, 155, 160,
    161
quantum numbers, main 68, 69,
    73n

races, three 85
radioactive decay, series of three
    31, 70
real existence of numbers 5, 11
reciprocal numbers 106, 107,
    123, 185, 186, 187, 191
relativity, theory of 27, 29
Revelation, NT book of 163
riddle of the universe 73, 169,
    202
rocket disk 50, 52, 203
rocket equation 203
rocket motor, new 203, 204

Sänger, E 51
Saros cycle 141
self-realization of infinity 72–3
sequence, decimal 165
sequence, linear 165
sequence of continuous numbers
    106
sequence of recriprocal numbers
    106
sequence of whole numbers 106
shell, zero 161, 164, 172, 174
Sierpinski Triangle 188, 193
silanes, higher 59, 60, 61, 62, 63,
    64, 66, 77, 78, 79, 81, 82, 85,
    203
silicon 18, 33, 54, 76, 207, 208
silicon atoms, asymmetric 62, 65,
    79
silicon atoms, steric 73
silicon, diesel oils with 81, 85
silicon hydride 19, 20, 58, 101,
    114, 203
silicon nitride 206
solar system 30, 54, 105, 139
Sommerfeld, A 11, 69, 70
space 17, 27, 28, 29, 45, 63, 104,
    130, 142
space mirror 108–9, 110, 121,
    157
space, four-dimensional 29, 111,
    128, 129, 154, 160, 161, 164,
    178, 180, 183, 185, 190, 191,
    201

space–time continuum 29, 80, 105, 111, 121, 129
square area 121
square law, reciprocal 104, 107, 150, 154
square time 121
squares of numbers 157, 164
Stark, J 145–6, 147
statistics of two-body collisions 184
Stock, A 59, 60, 79
Straub, D 205
structure of infinity 1, 3
sugar molecules 200, 201

technetium 30, 33
temperature 44, 206, 207
theology 2
thermodynamics 43, 44, 178, 190, 192
three-to-the-power-of-four law (3⁴)
Timaeus 108
time 17, 27, 29, 130
transcendental (infinite decimal fraction) 167, 168

trinity 144
triple bonds 207
triple nature 119, 121
triplicate 114, 127
twin planets 55
two-body collisions 181, 184

universe 168, 169, 190
Unsöld, A 60*n*, 148*n*

Vallée Poussin, C de la 166

wave packages 157
waves, electromagnetic 153, 154, 191
Wilson's law 198
Wycliffe, J 212, 213

$x^2 y^2$ geometry 121

yes–no decision 180, 184, 190, 191, 194

zero, absolute 44, 56, 117
zerovalent chromium atom 57, 58, 97, 144